This Is Infertility

KIRSTEN MCLENNAN

A STORY OF STRUGGLE, HOPE AND PERSEVERANCE TO HAVE A CHILD

INTRODUCTION BY
RUSSELL A. FOULK, MD

C&R Press
Conscious & Responsible

C&R Press
Conscious & Responsible
crpress.org

For special discounted bulk purchases, please contact:
C&R Press sales@crpress.org
Contact info@crpress.org to book events, readings and author signings.

This Is Infertility

Dear Fiona,

I hope you enjoy
reading this story
of our journey to
Spencer.

Love
Kirsten

To our darling son Spencer

This Is Infertility

Contents

INTRODUCTION

By Russell A. Foulk, MD, HCLD, FACOG
Medical Director/Founder, Utah Fertility Center & Nevada Center
for Reproductive Medicine & Nevada Fertility Center

Infertility can be a devastating disease. The thought of not being able to become pregnant and have children is likened by psychologists to being diagnosed with cancer. In the latter, one must grapple with the possibility of losing one's own life. Infertility leads to the possibility of losing your potential child's life and all the progeny that follows. It takes away the most important function in our lives, to propagate and carry on our genes to future generations. It can remove one of the most joyful experiences in our lives, to create a family and share in the relationships that it brings throughout all our remaining days. Infertility impacts all lives it touches, but the good news is that it can be overcome.

Kirsten's infertility journey is extensive and while not a common one, the emotional impact it had on her life is shared by all who suffer from it. Personally, infertility struck me and my wife for six years during my medical training, resulting in my career path. As a physician who has over the past twenty-five years treated many thousands of patients striving to conceive, I get to briefly travel with them through this emotional time experiencing the ups and downs of treatments, the hopes and despairs, the failures and triumphs. While I can develop the doctor-patient relationship during treatments, I often do not get to see or realise the personal story behind the people who suffer from it. Kirsten's book allowed me that opportunity.

Kirsten's journey is a remarkable book is several ways. I meant to simply skim over it one night before committing to a deep read later, but found that once I began reading, I could not put it down until I had completely read every page. It is a well written story of Kirsten and Ryan's long struggle with wanting a life-important event that most couples get naturally without trying. It educates and entertains. It describes the natural reproductive process, the reasons why it failed and the steps needed to overcome it. It entertains the reader with personal experiences that show the fear, sadness, frustration and, in retrospect, sometimes humorous events that people go through on their journey to parenthood. The most important element of the book though is the enduring hope Kirsten and Ryan had despite all the roadblocks they had to circumnavigate, including travelling across the earth to achieve their dream.

The book best describes the two most common emotional stressors that infertility creates, frustration and loneliness. With something as commonplace as procreation, one would think everyone would know about it. Unfortunately, it is still shrouded with mystery, myths and misinformation like the advice most patients get from well-meaning family members who say, "just relax, stop stressing about it". Imagine if that is what they would say if you were diagnosed with brain cancer; "just relax and you'll get over it". The reason of course is not malevolent, but an earnest attempt to help when most people don't want to talk about your sexual practices and sperm counts. Plus, in their mind, if you stop "stressing" about it, you will stop asking them about it. It is normal to be preoccupied with getting pregnant when you can't, just as it is normal to continually think about a splinter in your finger when it irritates you. Stress does not cause infertility, but the idea that it does demonstrates the lack of understanding in the general public and the isolative effect it has on patients. Through Kirsten's storytelling of their journey, we see the pain points they suffered from and the adaptive ways that both she and Ryan maintained their hope.

The ultimate success of having their son, Spencer, after sixteen failed IVF transfers, miscarriages and two international surrogacies is another example of how, despite the different journeys we all must take, the reproductive system is meant to work. Biologically if it did not work, then we would have ceased as a species long ago. But that does not mean the journey is easy for everyone. Kirsten's journey was tremendously difficult, but it demonstrates the importance of finding a good team to help guide you through the process. Most of the frustration patients experience is due to not being on the right path to success, or not treating the disease appropriately. In every case, one should know specifically why they are not getting pregnant, what they are doing to fix that and when they should expect success. If your advising team, physician, nurse or family member cannot provide you these answers, then you should seek a better team. Virtually all forms of infertility can be overcome to have a baby. All those who suffer from it should have hope that they will have a family.

Kirsten's journey is a wonderful story about how she and Ryan endured with hope, found their path and fulfilled their dreams of having their beautiful little Spencer to raise and love.

CHAPTER 1: THE BEGINNING

A journey of a thousand miles begins with a single step (Lao Tzu)

On 5 July 2019 at 11:49 am, our beautiful son Spencer John Wilson was born through surrogacy. It had been a long journey and like most things worth fighting for, it had been a hard one.

The American novelist Barbara Kingsolver once wrote, "The very least you can do in your life is figure out what you hope for. And the most you can do is live inside that hope". For six years, we lived inside hope. It was our bubble. We lived and breathed it every day. So, what did we do inside our bubble? At first, it was all about the medical treatment. I once counted how many times I had injected myself with artificial hormones: 700 times. And that was the easiest part. The injections didn't come close to the heartache and relentless disappointment that followed.

By the end, we had sixteen failed IVF (In vitro fertilisation) cycles, four failed IUI (Intrauterine Insemination) cycles, seven egg retrievals, two miscarriages and an ectopic pregnancy, and international surrogacy in two countries. But in the end, we also had our precious son Spencer, so we would do it all again.

Like any story of struggle and determination, there's always one great heartbreak. So, what was ours? That one devastating moment that left a scar? It was an unexpected tragedy halfway across the world, separated from our friends and family, where any chance of having a baby was cruelly ripped away from us. It happened in Toronto, Canada. Everything else in our journey I've made peace with. But when it's something so unexpected and unheard of—it can be a devastating shock. I'll come to 'The Canada Event' mid-way through our story.

I'll start my story with when I first met my husband Ryan in 2008. I was twenty-eight and working in Public Relations but for an insurance company, so it was far from glamorous. I was living with a good friend in St Kilda East, Melbourne (Australia). As two single girls, we spent most of our nights out or chatting on our apartment balcony while enjoying wine. I was happily single, and I wasn't interested in meeting anyone.

The night I met Ryan; I was at a bar in St Kilda celebrating my birthday when he strolled in with some mutual friends. At 6.4 feet and with classic good looks, Ryan stands out in a crowd. He certainly did that night in my eyes.

The first thing Ryan ever said to me was, "Happy Birthday. I have the same birthday, by the way". I was immediately taken aback. It felt like an odd thing to say. Surely, he could do better than this for a pickup line? With a boyish grin, he pulled out his driver's licence. There it was: the same birthday.

A couple of hours later and Ryan had won me over with his infectious energy, kindness, humour and sharp intellect. So much for being happily single, I was hooked.

When we first met, Ryan was finishing an advertising degree. He was twenty-six and studying his second degree. He studied Film first, but decided it was an extremely tough industry and he didn't have quite enough passion for it. To this day though, he loves to critique films and go to the movies.

Ryan had ended a serious relationship a year earlier and was happily 'playing the field'. He said that all changed the night we met. We had technically met six months earlier. After a work function one night, a colleague invited me to meet up afterwards with her partner and his friends. We arrived around midnight, but I'm embarrassed to admit, I don't remember meeting Ryan. The champagne I had drunk probably didn't help. But Ryan still says he remembers, "The beautiful girl on the dance floor with the black dress and long blonde hair".

A week after my birthday, we went to a local Thai restaurant for our first date. We talked and laughed for hours. I found being around Ryan was easy. No trying too hard, no games. I felt myself around him. The best version of myself.

I was flattered that night when Ryan told me that I was the most sophisticated and beautiful woman he had ever met. I almost choked on my spring roll. He was yet to see me with no makeup on and wearing tracksuit pants while watching reality TV. But the look in his eyes as he spoke, I could tell he meant every word. And I loved that he saw me this way. He made me feel special.

A few days later, we had our second date. It was on our way home when I heard a strange rattling noise coming from the car. Ryan laughed nervously, "The car's fine, this happens all the time," as he dropped me home.

Minutes later, he rang my doorbell asking frantically if I could drive him to the nearest petrol station. He confessed he had been running late to pick me up. Desperate to make a good impression, he had decided to run the risk. I still remember his flushed pink cheeks and panicked eyes. He was worried I would be 'turned off', but I found the opposite to be true. In fact, I found the whole petrol fiasco endearing. And it was in that moment that I knew this relationship would be different.

We married in November 2011 on a gorgeous sunny day with our close friends and family. They say your wedding can be one of the most memorable days of your life. Ours didn't disappoint. The band had everyone on their feet within thirty minutes with John Farnham's Aussie classic 'You're the Voice'. A drunk uncle, a friend doing the worm on the dance floor and a bridesmaid kissing a fellow guest in a dark corner—it was your quintessential Australian wedding. It was one huge party and to this day, people still tell us how much fun it was. Two days later we jetted off to the United States for a month-long honeymoon. Too many New York hot dogs, but so many wonderful memories. It was the start of our life together as a married couple. There was so much to look forward to.

About eighteen months later, we decided to try for a family. We had first talked about having children only three months into our relationship. One night I had mustered up the courage to ask Ryan. It may have only been three months, but I saw a future with him, so I needed to know whether he wanted children. Thankfully, he did.

As we were in our early thirties when we first started trying to get pregnant, we thought it would be easy. But then a year went by. Countless ovulation kits and pregnancy tests but no pink double lines. I was confused and annoyed. I've always been a planner and I like to be organised, and as somewhat of a perfectionist, I had chosen the ideal time for us to fall pregnant. This delay was seriously messing up my life plan. "What on earth is going on? Why aren't we pregnant yet?", I quizzed Ryan one night. "Damned if I know," he shrugged, disappointed.

I now cringe when I think back to this time. I'm sure for some people, you can pinpoint the perfect time to have a baby. But for many, it's impossible. Most of our friends weren't trying to have a family yet and I only knew of one couple who were struggling to conceive. Even still, the fact I thought we would fall pregnant easily was naive and showed just how far I would have to go on this journey.

Infertility can be brutal, raw and often lonely. It's frequently misunderstood. But for anyone struggling with infertility, you are not alone. There are many of us out there. My story is but one of many.

I am writing this book to share my personal experience of infertility. To give an honest—and sometimes brutal—account about the realities of fertility treatment, the IVF industry in Australia and the United States, and international surrogacy. I'll share our positive experiences but also our obstacles, disappointments and heartbreak. And ultimately what I learned from it all.

Note: I have defined the more technical terms on infertility in the Glossary.

CHAPTER 2: OUR INFERTILITY JOURNEY BEGINS

Don't worry about failures, worry about the chances you miss when you don't even try (Jack Canfield)

It soon became clear we needed a little help. We needed to see a fertility expert. To find one, I asked a few trusted friends who had undergone fertility treatment, "What clinic has the best success rate? Who is 'the best' specialist?" It wasn't long before I booked in our first appointment and nervously, we got started.

We were confident and hopeful walking into the appointment. Why? Because we were being proactive. We had a problem, and we were taking steps to fix it. It felt like we were in control. And being in control was a feeling I was comfortable with.

The specialist, let's call her Dr Jones, was warm and approachable. We liked her right away. It was at this appointment that Dr Jones suggested I take Clomiphene, commonly known as Clomid. It's a medication designed to help you ovulate. During a pelvic exam, Dr Jones found I had poly cystic ovaries (PCO). It sounded like a serious medical term, so I was convinced this was the problem and Clomid was the answer. Just to confuse things though, she told me that having PCO is different from having Poly Cystic Ovaries Syndrome (PCOS). The Syndrome is a complex hormonal condition. You produce eggs but you don't always ovulate. It leaves your ovaries filled with follicles which have 'failed to launch'. There are also some unpleasant symptoms like excess facial and body hair, acne and mood changes. It affects approximately fifteen per cent of women.

On the other hand, in my case, PCO meant my follicles were behaving abnormally. I had several partial mature follicles. Large ones. "See all those dark masses? That's your follicles", she said, pointing to the ultrasound. She really didn't have to point this out as you couldn't see much else. She counted twenty-four follicles that day. A normal ovarian reserve count is six to ten follicles. She went on to say that PCO meant that I may not be ovulating each month. Poly cystic ovaries certainly explained my irregular periods and often long cycles. But it's not that serious. In fact, it's common. Chances are you know a few women who have PCO. Up to a third of women have polycystic ovaries seen on an ultrasound.

To treat the issue, all I had to do was take a pill each day for the first week of my menstrual cycle. Too easy. I could handle that. Before we knew it, I would be planning my baby shower. We left the appointment feeling hopeful. Why? Because if you know the cause of something, you can usually treat it.

But I was wrong. A few weeks later, the dreaded monthly arrived. I was dumbstruck. I had taken the pill correctly, so where were the home pregnancy test (HPT) double pink lines?

Dr Jones tried to reassure us. "It can sometimes take a month or two. Don't be too discouraged if it doesn't work on the first go". Easy for her to say, I thought to myself. But after stewing on it for a while, I reminded myself it was early days.

I was shocked when my period arrived the following month. Shocked and angry. Was I taking expired medication? Why wasn't it working!? We had followed the treatment plan. It 'should' have worked. Another month wasted. My beautifully planned schedule was running off course, yet again.

The other thing specialists sometimes tend to gloss over are the pesky side effects of fertility medication. In comparison to what was to come—the roller coaster that is IVF—the side effects were mild. But at the time, it sure didn't feel that way: bloating, headaches, mild nausea and worse of all, PMS on steroids. All crap side effects, and still no pregnancy. I had meticulously followed the treatment plan and yet, all I had to show for it was a bad case of PMS. It didn't seem fair.

After four months, we realised this 'magic pill' wasn't working. Dr Jones had told me to only take Clomid for three or four menstrual cycles, so time was up. We went back to the clinic, where she presented a shiny new solution: Intrauterine Insemination (IUI). It sounded impressive. Known as a natural or 'less intrusive' procedure, Dr Jones would simply track my menstrual cycle with ultrasounds and blood tests, and at the exact time I was due to ovulate, she would pop a catheter with Ryan's sperm into my cervix. Ryan was less than thrilled with his part in the process. Little did he know, there would be plenty more plastic cups in dimly lit 'closets' in the years to come. But his embarrassment was a small sacrifice to make. This would work for sure.

The procedure was quick. A little awkward, but it mostly felt like a Pap smear with some mild period cramping. My legs in stirrups, Dr Jones made small talk about her weekend plans while she gently threaded the fine plastic tube into my cervix. We left the appointment full of promise. And then the waiting begun. Tick tock, tick tock. The dreaded Two-Week Wait (2WW): the waiting time from your transfer to the pregnancy test. I didn't know then how many 2WWs were to come, but this one sure felt long. The most infuriating part was there was nothing to do but wait. It was all outside our control. No appointments, no scans, no medication, no procedures. Just waiting.

Like many people, we were used to things being in our control. I've never been a spontaneous person. I can be quite risk averse at times and I like to plan things. Unexpected events or issues make me nervous. This is perhaps what I struggled with the most throughout our journey. I didn't expect it. And I had very little control over it.

My lack of spontaneity is something Ryan and I sometimes clash over. If a friend calls him and wants to catch up with us a couple of hours later, I feel uneasy. Because I hadn't mentally prepared for it. A true introvert, I like to know 'the plan' in advance.

In primary school, my Grade Six teacher wrote on my report card, "Kirsten is quietly confident". Spot on. I've never been loud or extroverted and as a child, I was quiet and reserved. I've always had confidence, or perhaps self-confidence, but in my own unassuming way. And I also don't like to let people down. I struggle with saying no. This has lessened as I've grown older and with going through infertility. Putting yourself first with infertility is often essential.

As an extrovert, Ryan is the stark opposite. When

unexpected plans arise, he gets excited. And I can see his frustration when I hesitate. Occasionally he'll even roll his eyes and sarcastically reply, "Oh, I'm sorry it's not in the calendar from three weeks ago Kirsten". Sometimes this annoys me. But other times I don't blame him, especially when we are free for the unexpected plan.

In the lead up to our wedding, we had mandatory counselling to be married in a church as Ryan isn't religious. I'm what you would describe as a 'lapsed' catholic. During my school years, I attended St Joseph's primary school in Elsternwick and Star of the Sea catholic college in Brighton. But as an adult, I've drifted from the church and some of its beliefs. Despite this, I wanted to get married in a church. It was a beautiful church, and I also knew it would mean a lot to my family. And so, off to counselling we went.

We're both in the centre on the introvert / extrovert scale, but the distinction is still clear. One afternoon at counselling, we delved into our introvert and extrovert traits. It was a light bulb moment and made me realise Ryan gets his energy off people! I'm not sure why I didn't realise this earlier. Suddenly my head was flooded with memories of Ryan being tired or run down, going out with a friend, and coming back home refreshed and energetic.

The counselling made Ryan appreciate that for me to feel rejuvenated, I need a day of solitude. I need to read a book, go for a walk or watch a movie. I love seeing my friends and going out socially, but by the end of it, I'm mentally drained. While we still argue at times over this, we've come a long way in appreciating each other's differences.

After a long two weeks, the wait was over. I was at work when I got my period. I felt sick. A tight ball of anxiety aching in my stomach. Reality was finally hitting me that maybe this wasn't going to be straightforward, and that didn't feel good. We had been trying now for about eighteen months. I was also surrounded by friends and work colleagues who were constantly announcing their pregnancies.

Social media was the worst culprit. My Facebook feed was an endless stream of ultrasound photos and blissfully happy baby showers with announcements like, "There's nothing like a brand-new pair of genes. That's right, we are expecting!" Or my personal favourite, "I like big bumps and I cannot lie. We're expecting!" Every time I would see an announcement pop up—and there were always plenty of them—I had an instant pang of sickness in my stomach. A year on, I deactivated my Facebook account. It was liberating. Social media never did my mental health any favours with its hourly reminders of the one thing I didn't have and deeply wanted.

We tried IUI another three times. All three cycles failed. Each IUI cycle cost us approximately $AU1,500. It's now approximately $AU2,000 per cycle depending on where you go. I didn't know these statistics then but apparently, on average, a woman under thirty-five has a ten per cent chance of pregnancy with each IUI; twenty per cent at best. Put another way, I had a one in ten chance. For women over forty, it's even more dire. There's only a two to five per cent chance. Had we known these odds beforehand, I think we would have jumped straight to IVF. I'm yet to meet anyone who has fallen pregnant because of IUI.

The final time IUI failed, I got my period the day before a good friend's wedding. I was flying home from Sydney from a work trip when I noticed some pink spotting. Blood. Damn it. Not again. That familiar ball of dread forming in my stomach. But I had to brush it aside. It was Friday morning, and I was due for an afternoon of bridesmaids pampering, followed by a night spent together in a hotel before the big day.

The pampering started with a massage. Filling in the standard customer form, one of the questions asked, "Are you pregnant?" Circling NO (wanting to write—"I wish, but what's it to you anyway?"), one of the other bridesmaids nervously told me she would have to circle YES. She was seven weeks pregnant. While I had assumed they had started trying for a family, I was still shocked. I'm not sure why. It could have been because she was one of the first of my friends to fall pregnant. And with that, came some confusing and foreign feelings. In my heart, I knew this was a friend who was kind and empathetic and who also yearned for a family. And while I was genuinely happy for her, I was also envious of what she had. I desperately wanted it too.

Back at the hotel, I had a little cry in the shower about our failed IUI cycle, and then I buried my feelings. It was about to be one of my best friend's happiest days of her life. Now was not the time to get emotional about my 'fertility stuff'. The wedding ended up being lots of fun. I also had the honour of giving a speech, something I really cherished.

But the night before was the first time I had 'foreign' feelings I didn't quite know how to handle. Jealously, sadness, anger, despair—horrible feelings that make it impossible to sleep. A constant dialogue started to play in my head: Why isn't it me? I'm doing everything right! I've put in the hard work. And of course, the overarching statement that would visit me on many more occasions in the future: This isn't fair!

Of course, so many things in life are unfair and I knew many people had been in far worse situations than this. You just need to switch on the news each night to see that. People suffer great tragedies; this wasn't one of them. And no one is immune from suffering. It's one of the few things we all have in common, it's universal. There was also so much in our life to be grateful for. I would often tell myself that it could be worse, a lot worse.

But who was I kidding? At this point, it was becoming all-consuming, and my emotions were overriding any rational thoughts. It may have not been what most would consider a great tragedy, but it sure felt that way to me. Because the thing is, once you decide you want to have children, you want them yesterday. Having children dominates your thoughts, it's all you can think about. Every day, every week, every month, feels long. Excruciatingly long. You feel anxious for most of the day. At least, that's how I felt. Because I was anxious that time was running out. And amid feeling this way, everywhere you look, you see pregnant women or mums pushing their babies in strollers. It's all you see. And you desperately want to be part of it but instead you watch on from the sidelines, and the sadness and grief grows.

I remember at one point I stopped going to the supermarket. Every time I went, I would see radiant mums with their happy babies or toddlers. It was too painful. Of course, I didn't know then we would have years and years of waiting and uncertainty ahead of us.

I was certain about one thing though. Whether our situation was fair or not, I would have to try and deal with my emotions head on and damn quickly, otherwise I would have no friends left. Because like it or not, we had reached that age in our early to mid-thirties where everyone was starting to have babies. And little did I know it yet, but my good friends would end up being integral to helping us navigate this journey.

CHAPTER 3: WELCOME ABOARD THE IVF ROLLER COASTER

Never give up on something that you can't go a day without thinking about (Winston Churchill)

Being Type A personalities, especially Ryan, we were starting to get impatient. If you look up Type A in the dictionary, you'll see Ryan. Throughout the years, I've been described as Type A as well. But not like Ryan. He's the extreme. Ryan is the most focused, ambitious, motivated, energetic and independent person I know. Whether at school and university, work or his personal interests, he's succeeded at almost everything he's put his mind to. And when he goes hard, he goes hard. He's determined to succeed.

As a general manager in eCommerce for a global company, Ryan works long hours. Mid-way through our infertility journey, we spent Christmas Eve in Vienna. We strolled through the Christmas markets as it lightly snowed, the glorious sound of church bells ringing in the background. It was magical. What wasn't so magical was Ryan checking his work emails. "There's no days off in my job," he joked.

He is fortunate to love his job though and if it wasn't for his work, for both our jobs, we wouldn't have been able to afford years of fertility treatment. So even on holidays in Europe, I had to cut him some slack.

Impatience aside, the desire to have a child was getting stronger. I had often heard the saying, "You can't miss what you don't have". While that may be true of many things, this wasn't one of them. A void had opened, and it was growing larger by the day. Still, we knew it was relatively early days and so we remained determined and optimistic.

Some friends had also battled infertility and through IVF they had a beautiful daughter. Not knowing too much about the daily realities of IVF, we met with them for brunch one day to talk through the pros and cons. They were clearly advocates and confident in the process, saying, "IVF can be rough, but you'll get through it. It's so worth it. Trust us. You need to do this".

After speaking with them, and seeing the happiness their daughter had given them, we knew IVF was something we needed to explore.

So, what is In vitro fertilisation (IVF)? IVF has been around for about forty years and is a procedure used to "…overcome a range of fertility issues, by which an egg and sperm are joined together outside the body, in a specialised laboratory. The fertilised egg (embryo) is allowed to grow in a protected environment". The embryo grows for typically five days and then is implanted into a woman's uterus (or a surrogate's uterus).

In Australia over the past forty years, more than 200,000 babies have been born through IVF. Infertility affects about fifteen in every one hundred Australian couples of reproductive age. More than one per cent of babies in Australia are born through reproductive technologies, and today there is at least one child in every Australian classroom born through fertility treatments. According to the Australian and New Zealand Assisted Reproduction Database, in 2018 there were 15,475 IVF babies born in Australia, with numbers increasing each year. In the United States each year, 55,000 women give birth to a baby through reproductive technologies.

There's no sugar coating it, IVF is hard. It can be gruelling and demanding. It can take multiple cycles, sometimes years, for it to work. You often need to be in it for the long haul. "It's a marathon, not a sprint," one friend had warned me early on.

If you are one of the lucky ones, you'll get success within one or two transfer cycles. But I doubt you'll feel lucky at the time. Relieved maybe but not lucky. If you're undertaking IVF, you have most likely fought infertility for a while. So, whether your treatment takes you a couple of months or several years, it can all be incredibly difficult.

IVF isn't cheap. Prices differ according to country but for Australia the average cost of an egg retrieval and transfer is $10k. Of this, you get almost fifty per cent back on Medicare (Australia's publicly funded health insurance scheme). But the costs don't end there. There are: your consultation appointments; additional tests;

any surgeries; medication (only the standard medication is included and some of the additional injections are expensive); and embryo storage fees. Given it usually takes more than one or two cycles to get pregnant, you can see how quickly the costs can escalate.

Chances are most people know someone who is going through fertility treatment: a friend, family member or work colleague. Today, it's estimated that one in six couples worldwide battle infertility. One in six! According to the World Health Organisation, "Infertility is a disease" and "…between 48 million couples and 186 million individuals have infertility globally".

And yet, it's often a silent heartbreak. Silence is perhaps one of the reasons that research has shown women dealing with infertility suffer high depression and anxiety levels. One study by Kristin L. Rooney and Alice D. Domar showed that infertile women experience psychological symptoms, such as depression and anxiety, at the same level as cancer and cardiac rehabilitation patients. The study concluded by calling women undergoing treatment "infertility survivors".

Reflecting on my own experience and talking to others who have struggled with infertility, the findings don't surprise me. The old truisms of, "the more you put in, the more you get out" and "the harder I work, the luckier I seem to get" just don't apply.

I had always been taught that if you work hard for something, you're more likely to get it. Hard work equals reward. Then along came infertility. It doesn't matter how hard you 'work' at it. So much of it is outside your control.

Looking back, the only thing in my control was being my own advocate. During the second half of our journey, I realised the importance of speaking up and challenging specialists when I needed to. It was my body, after all. So, I started to make sure I was always prepared for appointments and brought a checklist of questions. Besides being prepared, I also think it's important to get a second and third opinion if you feel you need it. I regret not advocating from the start but better late than never.

The other thing I always grappled with is that there are

no guarantees. Fertility treatment only guarantees the chance of having a baby. Knowing this can often make it impossible to stay positive and continue treatment.

And finally, IVF is a roller coaster of emotions. You can feel despair, anger and guilt. You're often bracing yourself for something to go wrong. I seemed to have a permanently clenched jaw during our treatment. Somewhere along the way, my dentist gave me a mouthguard to stop me grinding my teeth at night. It didn't really work. But you can also feel optimistic and full of elation. You can experience highs of adrenalin. Whenever we received positive news, such as having a high egg collection cycle, I always had a rush of adrenalin. Because it was hope. And hope is so powerful. It's intoxicating. But excitement one week and dread the next—working through those contrasting emotions, often for years—is mentally and physically exhausting.

An ABC news article—'IVF is big business in Australia—but these people are calling the industry out'—delves into the emotional toll of infertility. For their investigation, journalists Sophie Scott and Angela McCormack interviewed more than 2,000 women. Two thirds of the women they spoke to said the fertility treatment had had a "significant impact on their mental or physical health". Significant impact. The women told them, "There's the quiet but profound sense of grief when a treatment fails"; "It makes you think you can't get pregnant because you are not worthy"; "It still has the power to bring me to tears"; "When it doesn't work, then you're going to feel emotionally destroyed. I describe it as getting to the end of the cycle and stepping off the cliff"; and "When it fails, it is utterly heartbreaking... I have cried more than I ever thought I could".

Reading through the comments, I can relate to all of them. You invest so much. Throughout our journey, I sacrificed my health, my career and my relationships. So, whenever we had a setback or failure, it was a heavy feeling. It was all consuming. For me, fertility treatment was a gamble, and I was constantly thinking: What's at stake here? Will this gamble pay off? Or will I lose everything?

In 2020, an Australian historian Sianan Healy searched for scholarly works on women's experience of infertility. She was, "shocked to find there was nothing: no real histories of what it is like to be a woman not conceiving or being able to carry a child to term".

Disappointed with her finding, she started a three-year fellowship at La Trobe University in Melbourne to collect women's stories about the significant psychological impact of infertility. One point she raised really resonated with me: "I've been interviewing women who say they suddenly feel they don't fit in, that because they can't have children there's no room for them in the wider public discussions of what it means to be a woman…. There is also a sense of feeling a bit invisible, that's a big thing. They talk about losing touch with people and a sense of not fitting in, in the same way as friends start having children." I think many women struggling with infertility feel this way.

Besides the emotional toll and psychological impact, once you step onto the IVF carousel, you are also consumed by the appointments; blood tests and ultrasounds; medication schedules; and medical procedures. Some weeks it felt like a full-time job.

And all the while, you're surrounded by the one thing you don't have. Whether it's your friends, work colleagues, your social media feed or even strangers on the street, when you're in the thick of it, everyone seems to be pregnant.

During our infertility journey, our good friends had twenty babies, with many having two babies. And that was good friends. I'm not talking about friends, family members, work colleagues and acquaintances. If I included that list, the number would easily be in the hundreds. For the first few pregnancies, I felt envious and hated myself for it. With every announcement, I would cry, sometimes for hours. As time went by, I knew I had a choice to make. We were at that age; this was now the norm. Nearly every week, a pregnancy was announced. Nearly every month, an announcement was made by a close friend.

To help cope with the endless announcements, I started meditation and gratitude exercises. Ryan put me onto an app called

The Resilience Project. At the end of each day, I would select an emoji that would represent how I was feeling. I would then list the things I was grateful for that day. It only took five minutes—so simple and quick, but yet so impactful. Coupled with some sessions with my psychologist later in our journey, the feelings of resentment and jealously slowly started to lessen. I realised it was too exhausting and consuming to stay bitter. My good friends weren't becoming pregnant to hurt me. They wanted to have a family as deeply as we did. With every pregnancy announcement, until we were pregnant with Spencer, there was still some jealously, but it passed quickly enough.

And finally, infertility is a major shift in life's expectations. I had always dreamed we would have two children. 'Dreamed' is the wrong word. I selfishly 'expected' to have two children. From all reports, I was a good child growing up. I never caused my parents much grief, I was the dutiful daughter. I 'deserved' to have a good life, I 'deserved' to have children. One born when were in our early thirties and a second baby by thirty-five. That was the plan. It never occurred to me that I might one day have no children, no family with Ryan.

I now know life doesn't work that way. People may deserve things, but sometimes you don't get what you want. And bad things happen to good people all the time. Life can be a random lottery, and when it comes to your health, so much is outside your control.

The reason the infertility was such a curve ball for me is that up until our infertility battle, life was easy. I grew up in the Melbourne suburb of Caulfield and I had an idyllic childhood with my two loving parents, John and Suzan, and my sister Amy. We even had the cliché adorable yellow Labrador. My parents always worked hard. They were never extravagant with their money; they were sensible, and I always had a financially secure home and a quality education. We didn't need fancy overseas trips, or even interstate ones. My childhood was filled with many happy memories in Bright, Victoria—riding horses and playing mini golf.

My most 'traumatic' moment in primary school was when our beloved cat Goldie died peacefully at the ripe old age of eighteen. A full life in cat years. As a teenager, I loved school, had great friends, and enjoyed writing, dancing (Ballet and Latin dance), singing and music (piano). I spent many a weekend rehearsing for the school musical, a music festival or an acapella group performance. Yes, I had the usual fall outs with friends, of course, as most teenage girls experience. But we always seemed to reconcile the next day, so the angst was short lived. My biggest worries seemed to be what outfit to wear on the weekend and whether Dylan from Beverly Hills 90210 would end up with Brenda or Kelly.

And I always had a plan. It looked something like this: Get good marks at school. Go to university (Communications degree, double major in Journalism and PR) while working part time at a local bookstore and volunteering in the publicity team at the Leukaemia Foundation (a not-for-profit). After uni, travel overseas to Europe for five months with a close friend before starting my career in Communications. While working, study a Post Graduate degree in Marketing and buy an apartment in St Kilda East. And finally, meet a loving and kind man by my early thirties. Oh, and get married and buy a house together. Tick, tick, tick. It all happened. All of it. It's nauseating reading on paper how carefree and uncomplicated life was.

And then it came. Out of nowhere like a tornado. I couldn't cross off the final item on my list: have two children by my early-mid thirties. The problem with life going perfectly to plan is when something unexpected and difficult happens, it can blindside you. For the first thirty-two years of my life, I had escaped this. Lucky me. Most of my friends and family hadn't been so fortunate. I had seen many of them suffer hardship or tragedy—from illnesses to having to endure the devasting loss of a parent when you're only a teenager.

As one good friend once told me, "Life is hard. It just is. For some people, it's a relentless uphill battle. Expect disappointment and hurt. Don't expect your life to be perfect. Knowing this will help make life easier. And it will help you appreciate the good things, of which there are usually plenty. Try not to miss those moments". Wise words. Having been through infertility, I now appreciate this sentiment so much more.

So yes, infertility can be a huge shift in life's expectations, on how you pictured your life would be. And while more recently discussion about infertility is starting to gain some traction, I consider it is still not talked about enough and is frequently misunderstood. People often say the wrong things. And words can cut deep.

I once read a witty piece by Donna Dunn in Mamamia, 'The things you don't want to hear when you're doing IVF'. A hilarious insight. It's spot on. Here's a selection of some of my favourite comments taken from that article. And yes, I had heard all of these, many times over, before I read this article.

- **You just need to relax.** Really? That's where I've been going wrong. You're right, IVF is such a calming, relaxing experience. If only I had relaxed sooner, I would have seven kids by now.
- **Have you tried drinking this special tea?** Listen love, if I'm dropping ten grand per cycle on IVF, you can bet your bottom dollar I have tried every special tea, every herb, every acupuncturist, every diet, every positive affirmation and every other ridiculous miracle product available that promises a baby at the end. Admittedly the powdered Patagonian tooth fish broth imported from Peru was probably going a big too far…but you name it and of course I've bloody tried it. That's how I got to this point—the last dance that is IVF.
- **If you don't have kids, think of all the awesome holidays you'll be able to go on.** I'm a silly billy! I didn't realise that once you have kids all 'awesome' holidays got cancelled and you must stay at home and rot in a dungeon with your crying babies forever…

Once we agreed that IVF was something we needed to explore, we decided to get a second opinion. We liked Dr Jones but when it came to IVF, there were a couple of others in Melbourne who were known as 'the best'. We wanted the best. We needed the best. Why? Because we felt like we didn't have time to wait. We weren't necessarily old at this point, but we were impatient. We weren't used to things not going according to plan and IVF was starting to be a huge disrupter in our lives. It was also getting in the way of other plans we had. So, we wanted it to be over with. But despite seeing next an IVF specialist who we thought was 'the best', we went on to get a third opinion a year later. Our second specialist didn't properly diagnose me so if it hadn't been for our third opinion, I doubt our son Spencer would be here today.

If there is one crucial thing I have learned, it is to get a second, a third or even fourth opinion if you have any doubts or need some reassurance. In my opinion, the IVF industry in Australia is not regulated enough so it's up to you to educate yourself. Talk to others who have gone through infertility treatment so you can arm yourself with knowledge. Fertility appointments can be nerve-racking so don't rely on your memory. Come to the appointment with your questions prepared. And don't be afraid to keep asking your fertility specialist the same question over and over if you're not satisfied with their answers. In short, don't accept vague answers or platitudes like "it's not a matter of if but when" or "it's a numbers game". Not exactly helpful.

When it comes to regulation with infertility in Victoria, Australia, the key body is VARTA (Victorian Assisted Reproductive Treatment Authority). A statutory authority, VARTA provides independent information and support to people about fertility treatments. But as it's not compulsory for Assisted Reproductive Treatment (ART) clinics to report their success rates publicly, VARTA only provides IVF data such as the number of egg collections and transfers per year, not clinic success rates.

Many IVF companies today are listed on the Australian Stock Exchange (ASX). It's a billion-dollar industry, one that continues to grow. In the same ABC News article about the emotional toll of IVF, journalists Sophie Scott and Angela McCormack also investigated regulation in the ART industry. The article discusses the common pitfalls: lack of transparency around success rates is one thing that always bothered me. Reporting of success rates also seem to differ among clinics. The Australian and New Zealand Assisted Reproduction Database (ANZARD) report in 2017 found, for example, that the worst performing clinic had a birth rate of just 9.3 per cent, while at the top performing clinic, more than a third of women took home a baby after their first treatment. Clinics will also usually only report pregnancy rates, not live birth rates. That can be confusing and deceptive. And given in Australia clinics are not required to publish success rates, finding them—or at least current ones—is near impossible.

There's also the lack of individualised care. I often found we were paying high consultation and treatment fees, yet our appointments were brief, and our specialists wouldn't even remember us. You're often just a number. We sometimes even had to remind them of our medical history and where we were up to with our treatment! We also had a different nurse each time we went into the clinic. But this wasn't our experience with our last specialist in Australia or in the United States. We had in-depth appointments and the same medical team throughout. But from talking to others who have undergone fertility treatment in Australia, I think sadly we were the exception, not the rule.

And finally, there's the lack of transparency with diagnosis and treatment. This was a big one for us. It wasn't until seeing our third fertility specialist that I was accurately diagnosed. If we hadn't gone to him, I shudder to think how much more time and money we would have wasted.

Our second specialist, to be known as Dr Taylor, recommended IVF. She wasn't as friendly as our previous doctor. She was blunt and clinical and with minimal bedside manner, but she 'seemed' to know her stuff. She convinced us that we had tried the less invasive methods for long enough and they weren't working. I was also getting older. In fertility land, creeping up to my mid-thirties meant I was AMA—Advanced Maternal Age. I first read that on a hospital form when I was thirty-four. Boy did I feel old. I would also go on to hear from one of our fertility specialists, "By the time you reach thirty-eight, everything falls off a cliff". How bleak. It turns out 40 isn't the new thirty after all. I've since learned this isn't quite true as there are always options.

The appointment was quick. A little too quick. The time

in the waiting room, sandwiched among the other hopeful yet apprehensive couples, was not. An hour of trying to be discreet and awkwardly avoiding eye contact, and then in and out within fifteen minutes and off to pay the steep consultation bill. I would start treatment immediately.

Looking back, we played it all wrong. We passively sat in our appointment politely nodding and hanging on every word. We occasionally interrupted to ask the odd question but agreed with all the answers.

People have often described me as 'nice'. Growing up, my grandpa affectionately called me his little doe—quiet, dainty and gentle. The flipside is I've also been described as a fence sitter and not assertive enough. At one workplace, I missed out on a promotion because they were 'concerned' I wasn't tough and aggressive enough with senior stakeholders. I accepted their decision without a fight. Even though my opinion was—and still is—that you can be influential in most jobs without being 'tough'.

But to use a familiar cliché, 'I don't like to rock the apple cart'. I avoid confrontation. This has shifted since infertility and with growing older, but at this point in our lives, I was passive and trusting. Ryan is more assertive than me, although I think like most people, he also doesn't like confrontation. He'll only confront someone if he has no choice. I think the reason he didn't speak up during our early appointments is he trusted the medical specialists. As many of us do.

But on reflection, we should have advocated for ourselves a lot more. We should have come prepared with a checklist of questions. We should have challenged some of the responses or asked for more clarity. We shouldn't have willingly been pushed out the door within fifteen minutes. We underestimated what was to come. We trusted the fertility specialists too much.

My checklist of questions I wished we had asked:

1. **What is the success rate of IVF for women aged thirty to thirty-four?** One thing many fertility

specialists fail to tell you is that most IVF cycles fail on the first go. And that the first cycle is often considered a test run; a trial to see how your body will respond to the stimulation medication and an assessment of your egg count and quality.

2. **What is the timeline? In other words, how long does an IVF cycle take from start to finish (i.e., from preparation and egg retrieval to transfer). And what are the exact steps involved?**

3. **How many cycles does it usually take to get pregnant for women aged (insert your age)?**

4. **Is the miscarriage rate the same or higher with IVF compared to naturally conceiving?**

5. **What is an ectopic pregnancy? And is the chance of an ectopic pregnancy the same or higher with IVF?**

6. **How many eggs are approximately collected for women aged thirty to thirty-four?**

7. **How many eggs are fertilised for women aged (insert your age)?**

8. **How many eggs make it to Day 5 for women aged (insert age)?**

9. **What's the embryo thaw rate?**

10. **What are the medication side effects? How common is it to experience the side effects?**

11. **What are the key reasons of infertility? Besides egg quality and count and sperm count, what are the other key reasons?**

12. **What is the endometrium lining and why is it important?**

13. **What measurement does the endometrium lining need to be to do a transfer? What is considered the ideal thickness?**

14. **What is Pre-Genetic Screening (PGS)?**

15. **What is the cost breakdown?**

Before you can start IVF, there's the preparation. Here is a quick run-down of the steps we took before we started our first cycle.

Preparation checklist:
- **Paperwork:**
  - Police checks
  - Child protection checks
  - Consent forms
  - Payment forms
- **Mandatory couple's counselling**
- **Blood and urine tests for:**
  - Rubella
  - HIV
  - Hepatitis
  - Syphilis
  - Thyroid
  - Full blood count
  - Iron levels
  - Hormone levels including progesterone and oestrogen
- **Pelvic ultrasound to assess your reproductive system and check for any abnormalities, e.g.,cysts, polyps**
- **Semen analysis**
  - This test measures the number of sperm and their ability to move. A low sperm count is often a cause of male infertility. About forty per cent of infertility is attributed to sperm, with one in twenty-five males thought to suffer from low sperm count. Ryan's results came back normal
- **AMH blood test**
  - The Anti-Mullerian Hormone (AMH) is a hormone secreted by cells in developing egg sacs (follicles). Put another way, the level of AMH in your blood helps predict roughly how many eggs you have left and thereby the number of fertile years you may have. Women make up around forty per cent of all the treated infertility cases in Australia, with females over the age of thirty-five having a one in three chance of having fertility issues. The remaining twenty per cent of fertility issues are a combined male and female issue. My

AMH was 3.5 ng/ml, above average for my age.

At our follow up appointment, Dr Taylor joked, "You have enough eggs to provide for all of Melbourne". An abundance of eggs and strong swimmers but still no pregnancy. It didn't make any sense to me.

Two weeks of injections and a month of medication, how hard could it be? But nothing really prepares you for IVF. It is a big commitment. It can take a huge toll on your mental and physical health, your work and your relationships. Squeezing in scans every one or two days at the hospital before work to check your ovaries for follicles for potential eggs; the awful medication side effects; the egg retrieval surgery and recovery; and the transfer procedure. Not to mention the countless injections. For the first transfer cycle, Ryan did the honours. Every night, he nervously jabbed an injection into my abdomen. "I'm sorry, I'm so sorry," he winced each time.

This increased to two injections a day in the lead up to ovulation. Six months on, I would inject myself as if it was second nature. I often found myself doing an injection while tidying up or checking my emails and never feeling a thing. It's funny how quickly we get used to something.

For subsequent cycles, there would be up to four injections a day, tablets, patches and pessaries. For our first transfer, there was minimal medication as Dr Taylor wanted to check how my body would respond. But there were plenty of side effects. You know how with every medication there's a list of side effects? And how you often don't experience any, or maybe only a few of them? Well, with IVF it's the opposite. You can experience most of them. For me, I had bloating, nausea, headaches, abdominal pain, fatigue and weight loss. And of course, my old favourite, PMS on steroids. One medication stated, "You may experience feelings of hopelessness". That was a first for me. How uplifting. And all the while, the one confounding thought played over and over in my mind: Will this work? Or will it all be for nothing? Because it was all a gamble. IVF doesn't guarantee a baby. It guarantees the chance of a baby. And the stakes were high. If it worked, utopia. But if it didn't?

Here's a run-down of our first IVF cycle:

Day 1-11:

- The first official day of my IVF cycle was Day One of my period.
- I took a 75 dose of the Gonal-f injection each day. Dr Taylor gave me a moderate dose because of my multiple follicles. The nurse was quick to point out that I needed to inject myself at the same time every night for it to work. Given the injection was kept in the fridge and the time was 8:00 pm, it meant we were housebound for that fortnight.
- What is Gonal-f? It's a follicle stimulating hormone. Usually, each month the body naturally releases one mature egg. On rare occasions, two eggs. Gonal-f helps to stimulate your ovaries to over produce eggs.
- The side effects aren't pleasant. The common ones include headache, vomiting, abdominal pain, pelvic pain, breast tenderness or pain, mood swings, throat irritation, gas, flu like symptoms, diarrhea and nausea. Less frequent side effects include migraines and low blood pressure.
- I also took a tonne of supplements including vitamins A, B, D, iron and folic acid.

Day 6-12:

- Every two days, I would visit the hospital before work for an ultrasound and blood test to monitor my follicles and to check my hormone levels.
- The hormones they check include the follicle-stimulating hormone (FSH), progesterone and oestrogen.

Day 9-13:

- Towards the end of my egg stimulation phase, I started to take the Orgalutran injection every morning. This is used to prevent you from ovulating too early. Side effects include headache, nausea, dizziness and irritation/redness at the injection site.

Day 14:

- Ovidrel injection. Otherwise known as the 'trigger' shot. The injection to make you ovulate. The timing of this injection is crucial as it needs to be taken at precisely thirty-six hours before your egg retrieval surgery. If it's not taken at the right time, the whole cycle is disrupted and cancelled. No pressure!

Day 16:

- Egg retrieval surgery. This is in hospital, a day procedure where the eggs are collected from your ovaries. Under general anaesthetic, an ultrasound probe is inserted into your vaginal wall to identify follicles and then a needle is guided through. The needle goes into each of the ovarian follicles and gentle suction is used to pull out the fluid and the egg that comes with it. Thank goodness you're knocked out!
- While it only takes about thirty minutes for the retrieval, I was at the hospital for half the day with pre surgery checks, paperwork, and a couple of hours in recovery. Given I'd had a general anaesthetic, Ryan picked me up and took me home where I spent the next two days on the couch recovering. For two to three days after, I experienced cramping, bloating and gas pain (presumably from the general).
- Once the eggs are collected, they are fertilised. Dr Taylor recommended we fertilise our eggs using Intracytoplasmic Sperm Injection (ICSI). This is where a single sperm is injected into each egg. It is often considered your best chance of

fertilisation, mainly because there is no risk of the sperm swimming around aimlessly in the petri dish unable to find an egg.

The results:

- Eleven eggs collected. Given the low dose of stimulation medication, this was considered a solid result. In later egg collections, with a higher dose of Gonal-f, I would get fifteen to twenty eggs.
- The next day, the nurse called to say that out of eleven eggs, nine had fertilised. Apparently, this was an excellent result. On average, around sixty to seventy per cent of mature eggs will fertilise.
- On Day Five, she called again to say five embryos had made it to blastocyst stage and were being frozen.
- A blastocyst embryo is an advanced stage of development. Blastocyst embryos are graded—A, B and C. Simply put, A and B are the best; they have well defined and smooth cells. In contrast, C embryos have irregular and dark cells and few of them. But there's an obvious flaw in the grading. You are judging a book by its cover, not its contents. There have been plenty of beautiful-looking embryos that have not resulted in a pregnancy. And some terrible-looking ones that have made healthy babies. The only true way to measure the quality of an embryo is through Pre-Genetic Screening (PGS) testing. I'll discuss PGS testing later.
- Before they're frozen, the embryos also undergo assisted hatching. As the name suggests, it's where the embryo has a little assistance to hatch out. A laser is used to gently thin the outer shell of the egg (the zona). If the embryo can hatch out of the shell more easily, there's a higher chance of implantation.

Day 17-35

- From three days after Ovidrel injection until the pregnancy blood test on Day 35, twice daily I inserted vaginal progesterone pessaries. Given progesterone is usually produced during a women's natural cycle, the pessaries are needed to maintain progesterone levels during early pregnancy. Similarly, with the Gonal-F, the common side effects include dizziness, fatigue, headaches, mood swings, bloating, cramps and stomach pain.
- The side effects also include nervousness or 'feelings of hopelessness'. Of all my IVF medications, these pessaries were right up there with my least favourite as they always seemed to affect my mood.
- If you receive a positive pregnancy result, you continue the progesterone pessaries throughout the first trimester.

Transfer day—Day 22

- The transfer was the easiest step in the treatment cycle. I had my transfer in the morning and I was in at work an hour later.
- For the transfer, an embryologist prepares your embryo by placing it in a catheter. Under guided ultrasound, the fertility specialist then threads the catheter up through your cervix and into your uterus. The whole procedure only takes about ten minutes. The most uncomfortable part is having a half full bladder, especially with the specialist poking and prodding around. But a half full bladder helps to push your uterus down into a more horizontal position, thereby making the transfer procedure easier.
- On the day of the transfer, the embryo is thawed about an hour beforehand. For blastocyst embryos, approximately ninety per cent of embryos survive

the thaw. Given we did numerous transfers in our time, I was certain that at some point, an embryo wouldn't survive the thaw. Fortunately, this was one disappointment we never experienced.

Day 35—The pregnancy blood test

- Approximately two weeks after my embryo transfer, I went to the hospital one morning for a blood test to measure my hCG (human chorionic gonadotropin) levels. Human chorionic gonadotropin (hCG) is THE pregnancy hormone, the hormone normally produced by the placenta. In short, your hCG levels tell you whether or not you're pregnant.

Day 35, the day of the pregnancy blood test. I woke up around 5:00 am and I couldn't get back to sleep. I had so much nervous energy. Racing heart, sick feeling in the stomach and a pounding headache—there was nothing I could do to silence it.

At the hospital, as the technician drew my blood, he enthusiastically proclaimed, "I have a really good feeling; I think you'll get some positive news today!" If only it was that simple. But I prayed he was right. We would know the results by the afternoon.

I left work early to be home for the phone call just in case it was bad news. My mobile rang in the early afternoon, and I could tell right away from her monotone voice the result was negative. So much for the technician's good feeling. I broke down, crying incessantly. The hormones raging throughout my body probably didn't help. Damn you, 'feelings of hopelessness' medication, I angrily thought to myself. I called Ryan in tears, and he left work early.

Remember how I said my friends were essential to this journey? At this point, not too many people knew what we were going through, but I sent a text to the handful of close friends who did know. I kept it short, "The cycle failed, I'm not pregnant". Within minutes, I was inundated with phone calls and text messages of support. One of my good friends was on my doorstep an hour later, chocolate pretzels and wine in hand. Red and blotchy and wearing my favourite 'nanna' blue dressing gown, I was so grateful for this act of kindness. We were not in this alone. Those same friends I had started to envy had dropped everything to be at my side. Being a more private person, Ryan hadn't told anyone yet, but he was so appreciative of the support my friends were giving me.

My parents and sister also visited that night. Patiently sitting there while I sobbed and went around and around in circles with the same questions: "I thought IVF was the solution? Why hasn't it worked? When will it work? Be honest with me, do you think it will ever work?"

My sister Amy is a nurse at a hospital and for me that meant I could ask her unlimited infertility questions. For years. I'm not sure how she put up with me. To her credit, she would patiently reply each time. She said on more than one occasion that she wasn't a fertility expert, but I didn't care. She worked in the medical field and that was enough for me.

So where to from here? Throughout this journey, we soon found ourselves in a familiar pattern. The day of bad news, we were disappointed and often heartbroken. The next day, we licked our wounds and carried on. The dark cloud would lift, and we would wake up feeling clear headed and driven, wanting to fight this. We were stubborn and determined. We didn't want infertility to beat us. And having a way forward and the next plan in place, always made us feel better.

I called Dr Taylor the next day. "What can we do differently this time?" I pleaded. "Let's do a 'endometrial scratching'. It will mean a month off treatment, but a scratching helps improve your endometrial receptivity and hopefully will increase your chances of getting pregnant", she replied.

Your endometrium is the innermost lining layer of the uterus. It plays a starring role in our infertility journey, so I'll come back to it shortly. For a scratching, the specialist takes or 'scratches' some of the lining of your uterus using a thin catheter. If that sounds painful to you, you're right. A friend, who had a scratching a few months earlier, had insisted I take some Paracetamol. "Or even something stronger if you have it. Trust me, you don't want to do this one cold turkey." Sage advice. It hurt. A lot. Over quickly but very painful.

In 2019, a global study showed that a scratching doesn't increase the pregnancy rate for women. As one news headline put it, "IVF scratching: Are women putting themselves through a painful procedure for nothing?" It went on to say how fertility doctors should stop recommending it as of the women studied, 180 women had babies in the group with the scratching and 176 did in the control group. I shuddered when I read that.

IVF often felt like a game of ruling things out. Keen to not waste a month, Dr Taylor ordered a test for thick blood. She told us if there's an imbalance in the proteins and cells responsible for blood and blood clotting develops, your blood can be too thick, and this can impact implantation.

I've never been great with blood tests. I certainly have not inherited my mum and sister's strong stomachs. A small finger cut can make me squeamish. So, it won't come as a surprise that I was anxious at the idea of a thick blood test, especially as they would need to collect twenty vials of blood. Yes, twenty vials! Whether it was dehydration or something else, it took the nurse forever to fill up those vials. Almost an hour. A week later, the results came in. I didn't have thick blood. One more thing ruled out.

The following month we began our next transfer cycle. At my first scan to check my progress, the sonographer (ultrasound technician) mentioned my 'thin endometrium lining'. Not really knowing what this was, I wasn't too concerned. She had been quite cavalier about it anyway. But at the next scan, she made the same comment. Maybe this was something after all, I quietly thought to myself. A phone call to Dr Taylor later that day and we learned that the endometrium lining was crucial to the success of any cycle. *Crucial.* To break it down, an optimum endometrium lining is between 10-12mm at your transfer time. I was close to my transfer date and mine was 4mm. It seemed low to me. I started to research.

I discovered that with a lining under 6mm, it was almost impossible to fall pregnant or sustain a pregnancy. A lining between

6-7mm was not great either, but you stood a chance. Ideally, you needed above 8mm. One research study showed that with a lining of 6-7mm, the pregnancy rate was 7.4 per cent. For women with a lining over 7mm, it was more than triple, 30.8 per cent. The study only reported pregnancy rates, not live birth rates.

What is the endometrium lining and why is it so important? The lining is, "One of the stars of the female reproductive system, playing a key role during pregnancy". The endometrium is the wallpaper of the uterus and with pregnancy, it becomes thicker so that it's ready to receive an embryo and support the placenta. The placenta is the organ that develops during pregnancy to provide the baby with oxygen, blood and nutrients. So yes, the endometrium lining is "crucial."

What is the solution for a thin lining? Estrogen therapy. I pounded my body with estrogen. In preparation for pregnancy, the hormone estrogen increases blood flow to help your uterus grow and maintain the endometrium lining. Besides taking about ten estrogen pills a day—I wish I was exaggerating—I also experimented with some natural home remedies: soaking my feet in warm water each night with a hot water bottle balancing on my stomach while downing litres of pomegranate juice. I cleaned our local supermarket out. I can't stand the taste of pomegranate juice now!

It was also at this time that I tried acupuncture. It felt like millions of tiny needles were placed into my body. I looked like a porcupine. To my surprise, I found it relaxing. Acupuncture is a complementary medical practice that stimulates certain points on the body (using tiny needles) to help ease pain or treat various health conditions. It's gaining popularity with infertility as it is thought to help egg production and quality, as well as invigorate your blood to increase implantation. Many women have acupuncture before their embryo transfer. I was one of them.

There are mixed opinions on whether acupuncture works. A study published in the British Medical Journal in 2008 showed when women had acupuncture two days before a transfer, success jumped by sixty-five per cent. In contrast, an Australian landmark study published in 2018 in the Journal of the American Medical Association (JAMA), found there was no difference in birth rates. In this study, just over 18.3 per cent of the women having acupuncture had a baby compared to 17.8 per cent of women who didn't have it.

I was hoping the acupuncture would help nourish my blood and thicken my lining. I was also really getting sick of the taste of pomegranate juice! With each session, my acupuncturist would gently insert the needles into my abdomen, hands, feet, and even my face and head. She would turn the lights down while I laid there for an hour listening to soothing music, a scented candle burning in the background. Like I said, it was relaxing. The acupuncture seemed to be the only thing that worked on this cycle to increase my lining. With each ultrasound, my lining grew a little.

But not by enough. On Day 22 of my treatment cycle, we met with the clinic nurse to be told we would have to cancel the cycle. "It's not working, you'll need to stop all medication immediately. You'll have a bleed, and you can try again next month".

I broke down. The nurse nervously handed me a box of tissues and tried to comfort me. But I was exhausted. I couldn't stop crying and nothing she said made me feel any better. For twenty-two days I had tried everything. I had taken more estrogen than a cow and it still wasn't enough. I had barely moved the dial. My lining had started at 3mm and twenty-two days later, it was only 4.7mm. To put it in perspective, a women's lining starts at 3mm at the end of your period and usually increases 1-2mm a day, with most women reaching 10-12mm by their transfer day (around Day 16-21). I had a lining of 4.7mm and I didn't have to be a fertility specialist to know that wasn't good.

Over time, I found a cancelled cycle more upsetting than a failed one. I'm sure that's not the case for everyone but to train hard and not even get picked to play was deflating. All those appointments and medication for nothing. Absolutely nothing.

A sinking thought also niggled away at me: How will it be different next time? And how do you push a niggling thought aside? You can't. Well, I couldn't. For me, it was always there, with every single cycle. It was mentally exhausting. Throughout our journey, we had three more cancelled cycles because of my thin endometrium lining. They were always tough.

As the nurse had promised, I stopped the medication, and it wasn't long before my period arrived. For the next cycle, Dr Taylor suggested some different medication to help thicken my lining. This included daily Clexane injections. Clexane is a blood thinning drug that increases blood flow and so helps implantation. It was my least favourite injection as it always stung. And it left internal bruising marks on my stomach that took years to disappear. On this transfer cycle, my lining increased to 6.5mm. Six millimetres is the minimum required to do a transfer in Australia. As a lining under 8mm is considered thin, in the United States the minimum is 8mm.

A lining of 6.5mm. We were back in the game and ready to transfer. There were two possible outcomes. It would either work or it wouldn't. Or was it that simple?

CHAPTER 4: WHERE HAS IT IMPLANTED?

If your nerve deny you—Go above your nerve (Emily Dickinson)

'Pregnancy of an Unknown Location'. Yes, you read that right. There were so many things we would learn along our journey. That you can be pregnant and yet not know where the embryo has implanted, was one of them.

A few days after our second transfer, I started bleeding. Dread. And once again the universe had its timing. I started bleeding an hour before a close friend's baby shower. One hour before. I'm not a superstitious person, but I'll admit, the timing was uncanny. I felt like I was someone's punch line.

A quick sidebar about baby showers. Don't go. Unless it's a good friend's shower. And even then, see how you feel at the time or where you're at with your treatment. If it's a work colleague, acquaintance, distant relative…don't go! As one friend asked me, "Why would you put yourself through that?"

If you're not close to the person, I doubt they'll miss you being there. If you do go, strap yourself in for at least two hours celebrating the one thing you don't have. Those two hours will be full of excited squeals and 'fun' guessing games about the baby's birth weight, the due date, the gender. You'll be surrounded by the one thing you yearn for and would do anything to have. The one thing you are fighting so hard for. I realised early on that this can be excruciating. Then one day, I just stopped going and had to trust it would be okay. It was. With my close friends, I always went. My good friends don't need to be the centre of attention. Their baby showers were always intimate and beautiful. They also had an innate ability to make sure I was okay.

Back to the bleed. Convinced it was my period, I accepted defeat. I nervously went off to the baby shower, a knot in my stomach. But being around my friends made me feel better. I quietly told one friend what had happened, and she clung to me like my life raft, never leaving my side. She had suffered her own infertility challenges over the years, so she understood. Trying to think optimistically, I pictured my own baby shower and knew this baby was worth fighting for.

Back home, I cried hard that night. The clinic was adamant I still needed the blood test for pregnancy as many women can bleed during pregnancy. Ryan calmly kept reassuring me of this, "Remember what the nurse said? It isn't over until the blood test". I wasn't convinced. I angrily fought back tears while I not-so-politely told him to stick it. "I know my own body, Ryan! It hasn't worked, I'm not pregnant!" I cried and cried until I eventually exhausted myself to sleep.

I certainly didn't expect the voice message from the nurse three days later, the day of the pregnancy blood test. "The result is not what we were expecting. Call me back immediately". As it turns out, I wasn't as in tune with my body after all. I was pregnant. My hCG (human chorionic gonadotropin) was forty-five. And that was the issue, forty-five.

The number was low. According to our nurse, for the first week of pregnancy, a hCG of fifty to one hundred is considered a viable pregnancy. We would retest in a couple of days. Two days later and my hCG was seventy-five. As hCG needs to at least double every forty-eight hours for a viable pregnancy, seventy-five meant I would inevitably miscarry. We had been mentally preparing for this, but it was still gut wrenching. There's always the tiniest glimmer of hope to hold onto. It's what gets you through. I had thought that while the hCG had started low, it could miraculously jump up. I had read that that can sometimes happen. I was wrong. I was instructed to stop all medication at once and I was told I would miscarry. A day later I had a heavy bleed. It was over.

Or so we thought. I needed to have one final blood test to check my hCG levels. It was a week since my initial blood test when I went to the clinic one morning for a follow up test. The nurse called a couple of hours later to tell me that the hCG was still there. Worse still, it had increased. Not by enough, but it had steadily risen. A little help was needed. Dr Taylor scheduled a laparoscopy—a keyhole surgery to examine, or operate, on the interior of the abdominal or pelvic cavities. A laparoscopy has all the usual side effects of abdominal pain, nausea, light-headedness and sometimes a persistent cough and shortness of breath.

The surgery would give Dr Taylor a clearer picture of what had happened. She would also remove any endometriosis (tissue that has grown outside the uterus) and check my fallopian tubes for an ectopic pregnancy. A day procedure: off to dream land I went. I woke up in recovery from the general anaesthesia feeling sore and deflated, but at least it was over. We could close this chapter and move on. Or could we?

A few days later, another blood test. The hCG was still there and slowly rising. There was nothing showing up on the ultrasound and there was enough hCG by now to detect 'something' on a scan. A loud voice in my head started screaming: What the hell is going on? Confused and furious about what was happening and wanting some answers, it was at this point the term 'Pregnancy of an Unknown Location' was first mentioned. I quickly Googled it and came across a leaflet that said, "Pregnancy of an Unknown Location (PUL) can seem confusing initially. We hope that this leaflet will help make things clearer". I hoped so as well!

It went on to say that PUL is where you get a positive pregnancy test result but there's no sign of the pregnancy in the uterus, and you can't determine the location of the pregnancy. The location can include the cervix, ovary and various intra-abdominal sites. It's different from an ectopic pregnancy though where the fertilised egg has implanted in one of the fallopian tubes. In short, the embryo had implanted 'somewhere' in my body, but Dr Taylor wasn't sure where. Not exactly reassuring. She also stressed that it was crucial we keep a close eye on it as these types of pregnancies, "Can be fatal if you don't monitor it".

Fatal. I felt nauseous. We had now reached a new stage in our journey. We had committed to do "whatever it takes" to have a child. I just hadn't realised it meant risking my life.

It had now been six weeks since our embryo transfer. I was pissed off. We both were. I'd had blood tests and monitoring for more than a month now. I had also tried some Chinese medicine that my acupuncturist had given me to help 'move things along' to create a natural miscarriage. I gagged the first time I drank it. Brown and lumpy, and I think with some bark thrown in, it tasted horrible. But I was desperate to try anything. My acupuncturist dropped off the Chinese medicine, and a mixing pot to boil the herbs, to my home one night. She didn't have to do this. Being a caring person, she always tried to help me. But the Chinese herbs didn't work. I kept bleeding every day, often heavily, for more than a month. I felt like I was starring in a C-Grade zombie movie, stumbling around all over the place. I could barely make it through the day. And the hCG remained. It was stubborn. It just wouldn't budge. We wanted this nightmare to be over. We were both bone tired. But as all of this happened at Christmas time and the fertility clinic was closed for two weeks, we had to wait it out.

During this time, Dr Taylor's words plagued me, "Can be fatal…". I couldn't stop thinking: Will I wake up one night in horrific pain? Will Ryan be home, or will I be alone? Will we make it to the hospital in time? Yes, I was exhausted from it all but I was now also petrified.

The final treatment offered was methotrexate. Not knowing what that was, I turned to my old friend Dr Google and learnt it was a chemotherapy agent to treat cancer, autoimmune diseases and ectopic pregnancies.

Dr Google is not your friend, by the way. Stay off Google if you can. As one friend put it, "You get an instant hit of adrenalin, and you feel better but minutes later you crash down, and you feel worse. So, you need another hit. You keep on googling and hours later, it's 2:00 am and you're back where you started having learned nothing. And most likely feeling worse".

My sister also tried to sternly make this point, "Kirsten, the only source of truth are academic medical journals. That is all you should be reading. Nothing else. And for gosh shake, stay off those bloody blog forums!!" She knew me too well.

Methotrexate. The thought of it left a bad taste in my mouth. But Dr Taylor quietly assured me it was a low dose, and it would, "Kill off anything 'foreign' in your body". I hated her choice of words. Yes, our embryo had implanted in the wrong place. The place was foreign. But it was still an embryo, the start of life. And what if it had implanted in the right place?

Right before my methotrexate appointment, I cried in the alleyway next to the hospital. I didn't have much time, so it was only for a few minutes but all I felt was a wave of intense grief. I couldn't stop crying. I can describe every detail of the alleyway, of that moment. The graffiti on the walls, the people hurrying by, and Ryan calling me. It's funny the things you remember, the moments that stay with you.

Ryan called to tell me he had been slightly delayed at work, but he was leaving soon. I convinced him I didn't need him there. I fought back the tears and told him I was fine. It was just one injection after all, it would be over soon enough. There was no point him leaving work early. My mum would meet me at the hospital instead. Thinking back, I did need him there. I wish I had just told him that.

As the nurse prepared the injection, I overheard her whispering to another nurse, "They don't know where it is! It's implanted somewhere in her body, but they don't know where. It could be anywhere! Isn't that the strangest thing?" The nurse returned and gave me one injection. It was over. I had heard the side effects can be severe. For me they were only mild, some light nausea and a dull headache.

Ryan and I went out to lunch along Elwood beach in Melbourne that weekend. We just really needed some time out together. At lunch, I had a heavy bleed. Two days later, my follow up blood test showed that the hCG was back to zero. Finally, it was over.

I stumbled back to work the following week, quiet and withdrawn. A couple of weeks before my methotrexate injection, a work colleague injured himself in a basketball game. He had torn his Achilles tendon. A painful injury. So, the team at work rallied behind him. They set up a private office for him, encouraged him to work from home and offered to get his lunch every day. It was the least they could do. He got a lot of support. As he should have.

The injury had left him physically restricted and most likely feeling mentally low. But what about me? I was physically and mentally recovering from something difficult as well. The bandage across my abdomen from the laparoscopy procedure was still fresh, oozing with yellow liquid and mixed with blood. But more than that, I was mentally destroyed. I really needed a support team.

But no one talks enough about infertility. And in the office that day, it was the first time I realised the profound silence of infertility. Not enough people talk about it and what they are going through. I was one of them. I couldn't figure out why exactly that was. Was it shame, fear of pity, embarrassment, judgement or guilt?

After a few hours of trying to silence the noise in my head, I quietly pulled aside one of my work friends and I told her. Telling someone, even if it was just one person, felt like I could breathe again. She was horrified. I saw the tears in her eyes and heard the sadness and panic in her voice. But I also pleaded with her to not tell anyone. To keep it secret. Yes, secret. Every time I would look up from my computer though, I would catch her watching me. Her face riddled with sympathy and panic. She spent the entire day watching me.

While I struggled at work that week and felt invisible, I was almost resentful of all the attention my work colleague was getting with his injury. I wonder what that feels like, I thought to myself. Instead, I suffered in silence, like so many before me and so many will after me.

Infertility in the workplace is still not openly discussed. It's reported that seventy-two per cent of workplaces globally don't have an infertility policy. I'm surprised twenty-eight per cent do! I certainly have never worked anywhere that has one. And yet, there seems to be policy for just about everything else these days. So why is it so important? To start with, there are so many appointments and procedures, you often end up using all your paid sick leave. If you're ever sick with anything else, you must take unpaid leave. And then there's the emotional toll. Sometimes you need a 'mental health day'. Especially if you've had a failed cycle or miscarriage. But it's often left up to the discretion of your manager. Luckily for me, I always had understanding managers who empathised and supported me at work. This was particularly true during the second half of our journey. My manager was always supportive. Whether it was flexibility with my hours, working from home when I needed to or taking a day off, he made sure my mental health and wellbeing always came first. But from speaking to other people, I think I got lucky.

It's hard to know who to confide in when you are going through IVF or any fertility treatment. At first, we only told a handful of close friends and family. As the years rolled by though, more and more people knew. I found it too hard to lie to people. Once we reached our mid-thirties and we had been married for a few years, many people assumed we were trying to have children, or they would not so subtly ask us. But more than that, it's difficult to hide something that consumes your life. And then it dawned on me one day: Why on earth should we hide it? Whenever a friend has an illness, they often share their news. They rely on their close friends and family for love and support. The World Health Organisation defines infertility as, "A disease of the female reproductive system defined by the failure to achieve a clinical pregnancy after 12 months or more of regular unprotected sexual intercourse". A disease. Yet we hide it?

Regrettably, I was often too concerned about other people's reactions. Looking back, I don't know why I cared so much. Since our infertility struggle and I think since turning forty, I'm now less concerned about what other people think. But back then, I did care. I cared too much.

My good friends got it. I think back to how hard it would have been for them. Every time they fell pregnant, they would have wrestled with how best to tell me. Text, phone call, a group message or a private one? At six weeks, at twelve weeks? They wouldn't have wanted to celebrate too much in front of me and risk upsetting me. But equally, if they didn't celebrate enough, would I think they should be acting more grateful? And some of them wouldn't have not wanted to share something so significant and exclude me. Truth be told, they were always in a no-win situation. Depending on where I was at in my treatment or how the medication was affecting me, some days I would feel genuinely happy for them. Other days, I would feel sad or jealous and resentful.

Most of the time I knew my friends were pregnant anyway; I was hypersensitive to it. I was always looking for clues. It wasn't always obvious things like refusing alcohol on a night out. There were more subtle ones. One day I met a friend for brunch, and she ordered a decaf coffee. She loves her coffee so it was a dead give-away.

I will say this though, I could not have asked for better friends during our infertility. Open minded, intelligent and sensitive, they were always careful with their words. They acknowledged my pain and didn't try to hide away from it. I think this is perhaps the most meaningful thing you can do for someone, even when it feels uncomfortable. For me, the most loving words you can offer someone who is struggling with infertility are, "How can I best support you?"

My good friends would often ask me this. I probably didn't thank them enough but their friendship, love and support during this time meant everything to me.

As more and more people knew outside our close family and friendship circle though, the insensitive comments started to roll in. I had to remind myself that people were either awkward or impervious. Or they were trying to help us and meant well. The most common response was, "Be careful what you wish for, once you have kids, you'll never get a sleep in ever again (insert laughter)".

Jokes. Gosh when I think back, there were so many jokes. I would politely laugh but what I really wanted to say was, "I get up at 6:30 am for work each day (Ryan is at 6:00 am) and I haven't been able to sleep in past about 7:30 am for the past decade. But you do make a good point, is having kids worth giving up that 7:30 am Saturday sleep in? Lots to ponder, thanks".

The most hurtful and tactless comments were, "Have you just tried relaxing?" or "When you stop trying, it will happen". That was always a favourite of mine as I would think: No, when we stop trying NOTHING will happen! When people made these comments, I would often angrily think to myself, the World Health Organisation and countless fertility specialists don't think so, but thanks so much for the unsolicited medical advice.

I once watched a TV interview featuring the fertility specialist who helped us with our surrogate pregnancy in the United States. A renowned fertility expert, Dr Russell A Foulk, MD, and his wife suffered infertility for six years trying to have their third child. During the interview, Dr Foulk explained how people will say: "It was easy for me to get pregnant, just stop thinking about it, stop stressing about it". He continued, "Which is really difficult information to get. It's like if you're diagnosed with cancer to be told to stop thinking about it or to just get past the stress of it, you'll get better, which is a ridiculous concept. Infertility, because it's so personal and intimate, can be difficult to share with others so most people keep it to themselves and suffer in silence".

When I watched his interview, I thought back to how many times people had said those words, "…just stop stressing about it". I've always considered myself a calm and an even keeled type of person. When I was leaving one workplace, in my colleague's farewell speech he asked, "Has anyone ever seen Kirst flustered at work? I haven't. She is one of the most measured and patient people in the team, a reliable and steady pair of hands".

As a Corporate Communications Manager, there's often times of heightened stress and extremely tight deadlines. Yet, when I was undertaking infertility treatment, people were offering me advice on how to relax, as if I had undergone a personality transplant. This always pissed me off. People would say: "Just go out and have a few drinks"; "It will happen when you stop trying"; "Try to not think about it and just relax"; and "Have you and Ryan tried a weekend away?"

I would joke to Ryan about these comments, "Umm, why had we not thought of this earlier? Thank goodness someone, with no fertility expertise, has told us. How is there a billion-dollar fertility industry when the answer is simply a night away on the booze?"

At times, the comments stung. A lot. I wanted to shout: I wonder how relaxed women being abused in war torn countries were when they fell pregnant? Do you know that women in these countries fall pregnant every single day?! Although I wasn't sure that would go down too well.

The problem with comments like "just relax" is that it places the blame on you. Most people doing fertility treatment already carry around a tonne of guilt and shame and think to themselves: Is it my fault that we got here? Is there more I could be doing? What's wrong with me? When people tell you to "just relax" as if it really is that simple, it's patronising, and it makes you feel like it's something in your control. It's not.

It can also be a major blow to your self-esteem as you can question your ability as a woman. I would often think: Isn't this the one simple thing in the world, as a woman, I'm meant to be able to do? I'll admit this is something I struggled with. Infertility made me feel like I was failing. And I wasn't used to failing at things. Well, not when I worked hard at something. And of course, I was worried about what Ryan would think. Within three months of dating, we had talked about both wanting children. When we got married, I'm certain he would never had thought he may have married someone who would struggle conceiving and that he may never be a dad.

I often had to remind myself that people are uniformed about infertility. They don't get it. They're not trying to be cruel. In a misguided way, they're trying to help you. Sometimes I would challenge people and give them the medical facts. Other times I stayed silence. If there is one big thing I regret, it's the times I stayed silent.

Back to the methotrexate. Eager to move on and start again, Dr Taylor explained that the methotrexate needed three months to work itself out of my system. It made sense. I had ingested a chemotherapy agent, a poison. We couldn't possibly try to get pregnant again. Whether naturally or through IVF. It made sense, but it was still hard to accept. More and more of our friends were now having their first babies. And that aching for a child was becoming stronger. But we would have to hit pause once again and wait.

CHAPTER 5: FINALLY, A DIAGNOSIS!

Always forward, never back (Junipero Serra)

For anyone doing fertility treatment, a forced three-month hiatus is tough. Three months can feel like a year. Time moves by incredibly slowly. With so much of the process outside of our control, the one thing that always made us feel better was grabbing hold tightly anything we could and giving it our all. Not being able to do anything with our fertility treatment for three months did our heads in.

We headed to Bali for a holiday, a change of scenery. Most days you could find us lazily lying by the pool while taking a nap or reading a book. It was the perfect escape. I've always found holidays have a special way of doing that. For the time you're away, you can pick the life you want. For us, it was life without IVF. No appointments, no medication, no let downs and no heartbreak. For those nine nights, life felt peaceful. It was the beach getaway we needed, minus my frizzy hair.

The break also gave us some much-needed quality time with each other because infertility can put a serious strain on any relationship. We spent our days just enjoying each other's company. And we rarely talked about our infertility. A major feat itself as back home it felt like there were times when it was all Ryan and I talked about.

I had heard infertility is usually a make-or-break scenario. Like any major stressful life event, infertility can push you to your limits and as time marches on, your relationship can deteriorate. You can feel disconnected or even turn on each other, or it can make you stronger as a couple. For us, it brought us closer together. It also made us appreciate some qualities in each other. I always admired Ryan's perseverance, optimism, and patience. He said he respected my determination and resilience. When things got tough, he was my absolute, my rock.

But I can see how it can easily swing the other way. You are under a tremendous amount of pressure. There's the financial strain as well as many significant decisions to make: Should we keep going? When do we stop? What's the best treatment? What can we afford financially? Not to mention the mood swings from the medication. I often felt like a pressure cooker, just waiting to explode at any moment.

Earlier on I read an article with the headline, "Study: Infertile couples 3 times more likely to divorce". Three times! The study involved 47,515 Danish women suffering infertility for an average of seven years. The average study subject was thirty-two years old. Researchers found that more than one quarter of the women were either divorced or living alone by the last follow up, as much as twelve years later. A sobering statistic. About one third of these couples had not had any children.

This study scared me a bit and it was always in the back of my mind. So, from the outset, I didn't treat the mandatory counselling as a 'tick the box' exercise. There were times when I had to drag Ryan along to a session but once he was there, he found that talking confidentially to an independent person was invaluable. In one of our sessions, the counsellor suggested 'date days', saying, "You're going through an immensely stressful time. As a couple, it's imperative you make time for each other, and try to have some fun in the process".

I'll admit that she'd scared me with her pointed use of the word 'imperative', so it wasn't long before I set up a calendar of dates. Sometimes it was as simple as a walk along the beach or going to the movies. Other times, when we really needed an escape from everything, we would go away for the weekend or take a holiday.

Reflecting on it, she was right. It was an intense time and having quality time with each other was 'imperative'. We had arguments along the way of course, and some ridiculous fights.

I remember one of our fights on the way to the IVF clinic. We were in the car and Ryan started talking incessantly about starting home renovations. Our house was big enough for the two of us, but it wasn't if we had children. This made me mad. I thought to myself: Will we end up with a big empty renovated home? Will it be a constant reminder that we don't have children?

Thinking back, it was irrational for me to get angry. If anything, I should have been happy and reassured by his optimism. But for some reason that day, I didn't feel reassured. Instead, I was really annoyed at him. He looked on in utter shock when I started to hiccup tears and yell. We were pulled up at the lights and he nervously tried to calm me down as some people in the next car were looking at us. I didn't know them, so I didn't care. I just couldn't stop crying.

But that's the thing about infertility, it's highly emotional and there's so much swirling around in your head. Even the simplest—and most well-intended—comment can set you right off.

So yes, there were some emotional and irrational fights but gratefully, for the most part, we were a team and always on the same page.

Three months after the methotrexate, we were back to our game plan. We did another two transfers. My lining barely reached 6mm, but we decided to push ahead. Pregnancies on a lining of 6mm are possible (apparently) but they are rare. "Maybe we'll beat the odds!" Ryan had enthusiastically declared.

We were both optimists throughout our journey, but Ryan's optimism never faltered. Not once. He always believed we would have a family in the end, one way or another. I did as well, but I'll admit I lost my faith towards the end.

Both transfer cycles failed. The results of these two transfers were easier to accept. It was as if we were going through the motions by this stage. Well, I was. I already knew the odds were stacked again us. It was also after these failed transfers that we had our three consecutive cancelled transfers. For these cycles, my lining barely reached 5mm. Each time I felt angry. As I've mentioned before, I found a cancelled cycle harder than a failed one. Why? Because you don't even get a chance to try. And there's nothing more infuriating than that.

It was on our last cancelled cycle that I finally took matters into my own hands with our treatment. I only wish I had been more proactive sooner. On this cycle, my lining had remained stubbornly low and at my final scan, five days before our transfer, it was only measuring mid-5mms. While I wasn't confident, our specialist recommended that we still go ahead as it was, "close enough". Only, I had read that for people with lining issues, it's not uncommon for the lining to fluctuate. Given we were still a few days away, I asked for an ultrasound the day before the transfer. This was not standard practice; she tried to persuade me against it. But I was insistent, so she eventually reluctantly agreed. It was at this scan that we learned my lining had gone back down and was barely reaching 5mm. It would be nearly impossible to fall pregnant. With the minimum requirement to transfer being 6mm in Australia (8mm in the United States), the cycle was abruptly cancelled.

I was relieved I had insisted on the scan. But I was also mad. If we had followed her advice, we would have moved ahead with a transfer. And it wouldn't have worked. We would have wasted one of our precious embryos. It was at this point I realised how crucial it is to speak up and be your own advocate during your infertility.

On our next transfer cycle, I awoke one night with savage stomach pains and abdominal cramping. Severely bloated and curled up in agony, an hour later I had a sharp piercing sensation that was getting worse. Ryan insisted we go to Emergency, especially as I was on a tonne of IVF medication. A quick drive to the hospital at 3:00 am and I was diagnosed with Ovarian Hyper Stimulation Syndrome (OHSS).

OHSS is a side effect of IVF stimulation medication. The ovaries become very enlarged with fluid, causing abdominal pain and bloating. I only had what was considered 'mild' OHSS. I was lucky as it can be dangerous. One per cent of women experience serious side effects including blood clots and kidney failure. And in rare cases, women have even died from it. For me, even though it was mild, it was still painful and uncomfortable. But IV fluids and pain medication soon gave me relief.

The 'what ifs' plagued me though: What if it hadn't been mild? What if I been seriously ill? What if I had almost died? And what if it happens again? Will I be so lucky the next time?

Not too long after my OHSS episode and yet another failed cycle, we decided to change specialists. The OHSS incident had really shaken me. But more than that, the failed and cancelled cycles were starting to build up, but Dr Taylor wasn't suggesting any new treatments. Instead, she would talk in platitudes, "It's only a matter of time, it's a numbers game".

Not exactly reassuring. And extremely frustrating to hear. I would often think to myself: You're the specialist and we're paying you a fortune; can't you be more specific? What does "it's only a matter of time?" mean? How are you helping us!?

Through some research of my own, I was also learning that a thin endometrium lining was a problem. A big one. So, one day we decided to stop seeing our specialist. She wasn't helping us, and we were just wasting our time and our precious embryos. We needed another opinion. We decided to see a doctor (let's call him Dr Collins) who specialised in implantation issues. We were now onto our third fertility specialist.

At our first appointment, Dr Collins hit us with the hard truth, namely, thin linings are rare, usually genetic, and difficult to fix. In his opinion, "Only five per cent of women under forty have thin linings," he stopped before adding, "and we rarely know the cause".

I was aghast. And one question immediately raced through my mind: Why have we not been told this sooner? I felt betrayed by Dr Taylor. Five percent, difficult to fix, rarely know the cause— these seemed like pretty significant details to gloss over. I angrily thought back on the time, money and mental energy we had already wasted. And all our precious embryos—did they ever really stand a chance?

He went on to tell us that, as we had already tried the popular treatment solutions (Estrogen therapy, aspirin, acupuncture and Clexane injections), it didn't leave us with many options. We liked Dr Collins right away. He was honest and renowned for not wasting people's time. He gave us the facts straight up. He is not everyone's flavour as he doesn't sugar-coat issues and the truth can sometimes be difficult to hear. For us, the truth was refreshing. Finally, we were getting somewhere. But now we knew the root of the problem, what was the solution? He mentioned it's hard to know the cause of a thin lining. So how do you treat something if you don't know what's caused it?

It was at this appointment that surrogacy was first mentioned. Dr Collins said, "I strongly recommend gestational surrogacy. It really is your best chance of success". We didn't know too much about gestational surrogacy, and we felt uneasy. It seemed overwhelming. Surrogacy in Australia isn't common, and we had never met anyone who had had a baby through surrogacy. Or who had been a surrogate. And like most things in life, the unknown can be scary.

Ryan laughed nervously, "I don't think we're quite there yet". Through his nervous laughter, I could tell he was overwhelmed. I knew he was overwhelmed as that's how I felt too. I only knew about surrogacy because of celebrities like Sarah Jessica Parker and Kim Kardashian. I wasn't sure their surrogate pregnancies painted a realistic picture. I also knew in my heart that I wasn't ready to give up yet on being pregnant myself. And it felt like surrogacy meant we had failed. Like I had failed. In my mind, surrogacy was confirmation I was broken, faulty goods; we needed another woman to help us have a baby. I was redundant and useless.

I know now, of course, this isn't the case with gestational surrogacy. But back then, we had limited knowledge about what it was and what was involved and so the irrational and emotional thoughts crept in.

Noting our uneasiness and accepting our decision that we weren't ready 'just yet', Dr Collins made another suggestion—a stem cell procedure.

Along with being an implantation specialist, we heard that Dr Collins was renowned for being a fertility pioneer in Australia and experimenting with innovative treatments. The stem cell procedure was one of them. He carefully explained that they would collect my blood and extract my stem cells. They would then make a small incision and inject the stem cells into my uterus through my femoral artery, using a thin catheter. All the while I would be happily drifting under a Twilight sedation. The procedure would hopefully invigorate my blood flow and nourish my lining. There would be no adverse side effects. It would either work or it wouldn't. It was only one day off work with minimal recovery time. It was worth a try.

The other valuable thing Dr Collins did was order a plethora of tests. These included a series of genetic tests. Both Ryan and I were tested for individual genetic abnormalities. We were also tested for compatibility. If we were too genetically compatible (e.g., were we cousins once removed), that would be a problem. Among these tests, he mentioned Preimplantation Genetic Screening (PGS). In fact, he was blunt, saying, "I refuse to treat a patient who doesn't test their embryos with PGS, so it's up to you on whether you want to continue seeing me".

I only wish we had been told about PGS sooner. I was surprised that he was the first fertility specialist to mention it. In my opinion, it's the most valuable test you can do. PGS tests if your embryos are genetically normal. Australian-based fertility provider Genea uses PGS testing to maximise patients' potential to have a baby by reducing miscarriage rates and increasing live birth rates. It screens embryos to ensure they have the correct number and order of chromosomes—this includes twenty-three pairs of chromosomes. If a chromosome is missing or duplicated, an embryo won't implant. Or if it does implant, you will miscarry or in rare cases, the baby will be born but with a severe disability. Given chromosome abnormalities are the cause of most miscarriages, according to Genea, PGS testing is said to decrease the miscarriage rate by a staggering fifty per cent. Yes, fifty per cent. Also, according to CCRM fertility, a pregnancy rate on a PGS cycle is sixty to seventy per cent, compared to approximately thirty per cent for a cycle without PGS testing.

Prior to PGS, embryologists would assess an embryo's

quality through the ABC grading system. Many IVF clinics still use both methods in conjunction with one another. But as I've already mentioned, this grading system alone is not reliable as it only assesses how an embryo looks on the outside. One of our embryologists once compared the grading system to a book. A book can look pristine and perfect on the outside but once you open it, there could be a page or section missing. Or a page doubled up. This means that story is interrupted and doesn't make sense to the reader. Or, in the case of an embryo, a chromosome is missing or duplicated and therefore it won't be a viable pregnancy.

Dr Collins also insisted on doing a biopsy of my endometrium lining. It would be the same as the scratching I'd had a year earlier, but it would take slightly longer. I winced when he mentioned this, unpleasant memories flooding back. "Do we have to?" I cried, "I mean, it hurt so much last time. Is it really necessary?" It was. "The biopsy will tell us if there were any serious issues with your lining—despite the obvious issue of it being too thin," he replied.

As I took a deep breath and geared myself up, just like Santa Claus, he offered me a present, "But I can always give you the green whistle.?" All my Christmases came at once. The green whistle. A few sucks on the pethidine whistle and I was floating in a dreamy fog. He could take as long as he needed.

A couple of weeks after the stem cell procedure, I was home one night when I noticed the palms of my hands were blue. It was winter and I was cold, but for some reason, I began to panic. A lot. Heart racing and dizzy, I stumbled down to the lounge room to find Ryan. It's hard to describe the sensation, but I started to zone in and out, feeling almost outside of my body.

Barely taking a breath, I rambled off a million things to him like, "Something isn't right. My hands are blue. I don't feel well. I think I'm going to collapse". And finally, "Call an ambulance right now, I think I could die".

Sounds extreme, right? But I had never felt this way before, and I honestly thought I could die. Ryan patiently tried to calm me down. Taking one look at my hands and seeing they weren't that blue, he took me to the bedroom to lie down. A little while later, I was still dizzy and upset so he called my sister. Amy was over within five minutes with her stethoscope, thermometer and blood pressure equipment to check my vitals. Having a nurse in the family certainly has its perks. My vitals were fine. She then gently told me I was most likely having a panic attack. Later she would tell me she was surprised it had taken me this long to have one.

As a nurse, Amy has a strong sense of order and calmness about her. She's methodical and careful. She always runs on time and has little tolerance for people who are late. It's something we've argued over before, especially considering I'm punctual myself and yet she's been annoyed at me at times for being only five minutes late! But timekeeper aside, she's incredibly kind and loyal.

Amy is also brave. If there's a fight or flight situation, she'll fight. One day working at McDonalds as a teenager, a man tried to rob her at the drive through. He forcefully grabbed her arm and demanded she hand over the register cash. But instead of running away or freezing, she jammed his hand in the register, hit the alarm, and yelled for help. Dumbfounded by her reaction, he froze and was caught. She was a hero. She hadn't thought twice about responding this way, it was instinctual. So, the night of my intense panic attack, Amy was the perfect person to have by my side.

A panic attack is described as a sudden episode of intense fear that triggers severe physical reactions. In many cases when you have one, you think you're having a heart attack or even dying. That seemed to be the case with me. I had mistakenly thought panic attacks must happen when you are right in the middle of a traumatic event or if you received some terrible news. That the shock of something horrific would trigger one. But that isn't usually the case. When you are going through something painful or traumatic, your subconscious can store those emotions away. And then they can come 'out of the blue'. For me, it was during a quiet Saturday night when we were at home relaxing.

Lying on the bed next to me, Amy put on one of my favourite escapist movies *The Devil Wears Prada*. She chatted to me the entire time, "I can't stand her! Why is she so mean? Poor Andy.

What do you think?" I was straight onto her. "I know what you're doing! You're trying to distract me," I cried.

She was, and it was working. An hour later, and I felt better. Very fatigued but the heart palpitations and nauseous had subsided, and I was falling asleep. Amy stayed with me for most of the night.

That was the worst panic attack I would have. I went on to have several other minor ones in the years to come but as I knew what to expect, I would try to calm myself down each time. I would take a few deep breaths, distract myself with a trashy reality TV show, call someone or listen to a mediation app. The attacks were always unpleasant but not terrifying like the first one. To be one hundred per cent sure it was a panic attack, I visited my General Practitioner the following week. He confirmed my sister's diagnosis but to alleviate any anxieties I had about having a heart condition—which I had diagnosed myself via Dr Google—he ordered an electrocardiogram and an echocardiogram (ultrasound) to check my heart. The results were clear, of course, but it was good for my peace of mind.

CHAPTER 6: THE MISSED MISCARRIAGE

No one ever told me that grief felt so much like fear (C.S Lewis)

A month after the stem cell procedure, we were ready to try again. Close monitoring of my lining had showed it had increased. The procedure hadn't been for nothing. For this transfer cycle, it reached 6.5mm. Hooray! We transferred in a Grade A PGS embryo. You can't get better than that. It seemed like a winner to us.

The dreaded Two-Week Wait—what many have described as the longest two weeks of their lives. But we were more confident than we had been for a while. Surely with the thicker lining and top-notch embryo, we would fall pregnant. Even though I was optimistic, I had taken enough bad news phone calls, so for this one, the nurse called Ryan. The plan was simple. He would take the call and when I got home from work, he would tell me the news.

The nurse called Ryan around 1:00 pm and too excited not to share, he deviated from the plan. I was in a meeting when I got Ryan's text message. Somewhere sandwiched between about thirty excited emojis were the words, "We're pregnant!!! Call me as soon as you get this!!!!"

The high was enormous. The problem is, when you get positive news with IVF, the exhilaration is quickly followed by continuous perpetual anxiety. For the next twenty-four hours, Ryan and I celebrated. We told our parents and a handful of close friends. We talked about our due date, when and how we would announce our news, the hospital where I would give birth, etc. The next day, dread set in. The high had been too intense and now I was petrified of something going wrong. The lining measurement haunted me. Yes, it was enough to transfer, but it wasn't the 'ideal' thickness. We wouldn't have even been allowed to do the transfer if we lived in the United States. Falling pregnant was one thing, but the lining was crucial to sustaining the pregnancy. As one specialist told us, "You need healthy and rich soil for a plant to grow".

A follow up blood test was scheduled a week later, at week five, to check my hCG and progesterone hormone levels. The nurse called in the early afternoon to say the levels were strong and everything was tracking along as expected. Relief and excitement filled me once more. The next day, angst again. This pattern continued until the day of our first ultrasound at week seven.

We booked an early scan before work. A friend texted me on the way in, saying, "Big day, how exciting!! You deserve this so much (surrounded by many happy emojis)". She was right, it was a big day. It was the furthest we had ever come. It was an important milestone to acknowledge. But I felt uneasy; we both did.

That's the problem with infertility, you expect things to go wrong. After a few setbacks, it's incredibly hard to stay positive. Because you also know if you're too positive and hopeful and things don't work out, it can be a crushing blow. It can be extremely difficult to pick yourself back up.

I remember speaking to one friend after her failed transfer. They had been doing IVF for a couple of years. When she found out the news, she told me she sank to the floor, started crying and she couldn't get back up, her husband trying helplessly to pick her up. But she couldn't move. She was stuck to the floor. The sadness and grief had been too much, and she spent hours sobbing in that one spot. That image of her broke my heart. And it was so relatable. Anyone going through infertility has had those moments, the times when it has been so incredibly hard to get back up again.

Once we arrived at the clinic, we were led into a small dark ultrasound room with no natural light, the walls closing in on us. My legs in the stirrups, the nurse popped up the probe for the scan. I'll never forget the look on her face—deadpan, not a shred of emotion. I felt sick. She asked how far along we were. "Just over seven weeks", we nervously replied in unison. A few moments later she said in a slow and measured tone, "The thing is, the baby's heartbeat is too slow. It's also measuring too small for 7.3 weeks. And the gestational sac is an abnormal shape, it's not round. I'm really sorry but I don't think your pregnancy is viable".

I burst into tears. Immediately, I started to beat myself up: Of course, it hasn't worked. Why did you let yourself get so excited this time? You're so stupid. You should know better by now.

She called for a second opinion and the next doctor confirmed her diagnosis. The pregnancy was not viable. We would inevitably miscarry. In that dreary small room with no windows, I vowed we would never have another scan in that depressing room.

On the drive home, I felt numb. Not sad, not angry, just numb. My mind was grappling with what had happened, trying to make sense of it. The nurse had explained that we had had a 'missed miscarriage' or 'silent miscarriage'. This is where the baby has either died or not developed but as you don't experience the usual miscarriage symptoms of bleeding and cramping, you never know. For many women, the pregnancy hormones continue to be high and so you still feel pregnant. A cruel trick. Even a home pregnancy test will show a positive result. So, you usually don't find out until an ultrasound.

In the same monotone voice as the nurse, I called my parents. They were over by the time we got home. I also texted one of my good friends and within a couple of hours, a large box of delicious cupcakes was at our doorstep. It was these acts of kindness that always helped us get through the harder times.

The nurse asked us to come back later that week, at almost eight weeks, for a follow up scan. Feeling vulnerable and raw, we went in for our next scan. Trembling all over, Ryan squeezed my hand tightly while she inserted the ultrasound probe. Silence. There was no longer a heartbeat. The baby had passed.

We had expected this would be the outcome, but you always hold out hope. And I had prayed that morning for a miracle. My prayers always went something like this: Please God, if you bless us with a baby, I promise I will be the best mum ever. I will also make sure I treat everyone with kindness, and I'll do more to help people, I'll do whatever you want me to do. Just please, please let it work this time, I'm begging you.

But my prayers weren't answered that day.

The nurse gently told us we had a choice to make. We

could wait and let my body expel the baby naturally, which could happen any day or take a few weeks, or have a D&C. We opted for the D&C. Known as Dilation and Curettage, the dilation refers to opening the cervix and the curette refers to removing the contents of the uterus. This meant a lower risk of infection and we could also biopsy the embryo to get any critical genetic insights. But most of all, the D&C would mean it was over and we could move on.

The D&C was on a Thursday, the day before Good Friday. Five days later, I was due to start a new job. The job was with a former colleague who had brought me across to his new workplace. Being a friend of many years, I explained what had happened and he understood. As my manager, on my first day at work, he continued to tell me to take all the time I needed and to go home early. He definitely went above and beyond at work with supporting me during this time. And in the years to come.

Miscarriages are common, but it doesn't make them any less heartbreaking. It's estimated that fifteen per cent of confirmed pregnancies end in miscarriage. Yet from talking to my friends, I would say the number is higher. Many women will experience a miscarriage. Whether the pregnancy happened naturally or through fertility treatment, after a month of trying to conceive or after five years, or whether the baby passed at five weeks or twelve weeks, it really doesn't matter. A loss is a loss. It is the loss of what could have been. In my experience, it's a suffering that doesn't compare to anything else. It rips you open and leaves you feeling raw, confused, lonely and sometimes even guilty. You can feel at peace with it one day and accepting of what has happened and then without any warning, you can be an emotional wreck the next day. For me, I found that the only thing that helped was to acknowledge my pain and not push it aside; to not beat myself up about what had happened; and to not give myself a time limit to grieve. And above all else, to not suffer in silence.

In the days that followed, we could have opened a florist. There were daily flower deliveries and care packages. My good friends called or messaged every day. Mindful of giving me space but also reminding me they were here to talk, whenever I was ready. One of my closest friends, my former housemate in St Kilda, was living in Germany at the time. Physically far away yet always present. One of my most compassionate and empathetic friends, she would always check in with me via WhatsApp messages and Skype calls. After the miscarriage, she sent me a beautifully handwritten letter. I hadn't received a letter for years, it felt so personal and special. A few years on, she gave me a friendship gift and a card that said, "It will happen". These three simple words became my mantra during the final stages of our journey. I pinned that card on our study noticeboard and looked at it every day until Spencer was born.

I had spent the last few days on the couch, or in bed, so on Easter Sunday, Ryan persuaded me to meet a friend for brunch to get me out of the house, clear my head and talk to someone. One of my good friends picked me up, showered me in Easter eggs and drove us to a quiet café. Having endured her own infertility battle, and now with a beautiful son, she was the right person to talk to. We spent hours at that café, talking candidly about everything. We enjoyed a pot of tea after pot of tea—I think the waiter was baffled that we were sitting there for hours, just sipping our cups of tea. But there was so much to talk about. I could have talked to her for days.

Looking back, talking about what you're going through and what you're feeling is incredibly therapeutic. It's essential. And that day, I needed to get so much off my chest. I wanted to talk about my heartbreak but also my fears. My fear that the fertility treatment was never going to work. My fear that I would never hold our baby in my arms, and I would never be a mum. And my fear that Ryan would never be a dad because of me, and that he may decide one day to leave me and find someone who could give him a child.

I always found talking to someone who knew exactly what I was going through, was an enormous comfort. And on that day, she knew exactly what to say and when to say it. She was the perfect support.

I was always appreciative of my good friends during our infertility, but I also realised early on that if there's also someone you can talk to who has also experienced infertility, that's invaluable. Like most things in life, the only people who will only ever fully understand IVF or any fertility treatment, are the ones who have experienced it themselves.

A couple of weeks after the D&C, Dr Collins called to give me the biopsy results. The baby had been genetically normal. The baby was perfect. The baby was a girl. I wish I hadn't found out the gender as it was impossible to not picture life with a baby girl, but it was too late. But more than that, it was another confirmation that the issue was me. Genetically normal embryos were being transferred in. Each egg collection, the specialist would retrieve an above average number of eggs for my age. When they tested them for chromosome abnormalities using PGS, eighty to one hundred per cent came back normal. So, it wasn't the embryos that were the problem. It was the carrier. It was me.

A strange guilt started to eat away at me. The rational part of my brain said how it couldn't be helped. My thin endometrium lining was genetic. It was indiscriminate. There was nothing I could do that I hadn't done already. But the irrational part was screaming: What am I doing wrong? What's wrong with me? Why can't I just do the one 'simple' thing that women are supposed to be able to do?

It was an awful feeling. Something that was meant to be the most natural thing in the world for a woman, and I couldn't do it. I felt broken. I felt like I was letting everyone down. I thought to myself, do we need the help of a gestational surrogate after all? The help of a woman who isn't 'broken'?

At work earlier that month, a friend had told me about one of our work colleagues. He and his wife were going through IVF. But his wife wasn't coping well. She was experiencing horrible side effects from the medication and the toll of infertility was impacting her greatly. It was affecting him as well, but his wife was really struggling. They were having some horrendous fights and often, she was in tears. He admitted guiltily to my friend he was considering ending their marriage. Infertility had changed them both too much and it had changed their relationship. And the fertility treatment wasn't working. He really wanted children, but at what cost?

With all this swimming around my head and my work

colleague's story fresh in my mind, I broke down to Ryan one night. He was on the couch watching his beloved Sydney Swans, an Australian Football League (AFL) team, when I calmly asked if he had a minute—I would be brief. "Not the best time Kirst, there's only five minutes left in the third quarter and it's a close game. If you can wait a few more minutes and..." I couldn't wait, so I abruptly cut him off. With a racing heart and almost breathless, I cried, "It's all my fault! If you were married to someone else, you would be a dad by now. I'm taking that away from you. I bet you wish you had never married me. I'll understand if you want to leave me".

As I spoke, I thought about all our friends. I thought back to the times when we were at BBQs—Ryan watching our friend's husbands playing with their kids, everyone looking so happy. Did he feel jealous when he saw this? Did he wonder why his wife couldn't give that to him? Did he feel resentful? Did he think: 'When will that be us?' And did he feel scared about how life would be without kids?

Whether he ever felt resentful or scared, I'll never know. Because he never told me. Not once did he bring it up. Not even during our ridiculous fights or in our moments of heated discussion.

Ryan is good at managing his emotions, but I can always tell if he's hiding something. It's usually when he avoids looking at me. And that night, he looked me straight in the eyes and with compassion he laughed, saying, "Don't be an idiot. I didn't marry you to have children. If we never have children, we'll still be happy. As long as we have each other, we'll be fine".

It might sound like a cheesy Hallmark movie moment, but it was just what I needed to hear. If anything, he just looked confused by my outburst. And he also looked really worried that I was so upset. And of course, he was right. And if the roles were reversed, I would feel the same way.

The next few weeks were rough. I was still processing it all. I felt vulnerable and confused. I kept searching for answers, trying to make sense of it. A counsellor once said to me that IVF can be like carrying an empty backpack and marching up a steep hill. It's okay at first, the backpack is empty, and you are capable and committed to walking up the hill. Part of you is even excited about the possibilities that lay ahead. But as you go along, you keep adding to your backpack. You don't take anything out though; you just keep piling in new stuff on top of the old and it gradually gets heavier. You continue to climb the hill, but the weight starts to slow you down. It's like an anchor. It becomes more difficult, sometimes impossible, to keep moving forward.

We had to have three months off treatment before we could try again. Time off was always difficult. Only two weeks into my new job and one Friday I started to feel sick. Convinced I was getting a cold, I bought some chicken pho for lunch and some cold and flu pills at the pharmacy. Yes, that would cure me! But that weekend I felt rotten. I couldn't remember ever feeling so ill. Maybe in Year Nine when I missed my school camp because I had the flu.

When I woke up Monday morning, I felt faint but determined to get to work. I didn't want to be 'that person' who starts a new job and calls in sick only two weeks later. I'd rather drag myself in. But after finishing my shower, I could barely hold myself up. Let alone catch a crowded train into the city. I didn't want to let anyone down, but I didn't have a choice. My body had spoken for me. I reluctantly called in sick and went to see my General Practitioner (GP).

Breathing in and out, I heard an unusual wheezing sound. "That doesn't sound good," my GP muttered, "It sounds like it could be pneumonia".

I was confused. I thought to myself, Pneumonia, really? Isn't that an illness mainly reserved for the elderly or heavy smokers? And yet, here I was, mid-thirties and healthy. I hadn't even taken antibiotics since 2002. A quick x-ray confirmed his diagnosis. I had pneumonia.

I was rushed off to hospital that day. I spent the next five nights being treated for pneumonia and pleurisy. Pleurisy is an inflammation of the tissues that line the lung and cavity. It can cause chest pain that worsens during breathing. That explained a lot. I had felt like there were a tonne of bricks resting on my chest. A few times I had panicked when I couldn't properly catch my breath.

Not old, not a smoker. Each day the doctor at the hospital repeated the same question, "Are you a smoker? Even socially? Are you sure you don't smoke? When was the last time you had a cigarette?" She always looked suspicious when I said no. "Does a quick drag of a cigarette in my first year of university count? I only tried it once, didn't care for it much, but I'm starting to regret it now," I joked.

She was not amused. No, it did not. Yes, it was a bit of mystery to the doctors that I had pneumonia. But not to me. I had experienced pain recently and I hadn't quite dealt with it. I had opened my backpack, shoved it in down the bottom somewhere and had firmly closed it. But my body hadn't forgotten. It had stored it. It had clung onto it and my immune system had been compromised. It was a timely reminder of the importance of self-care, something I would go on to prioritise in the future. The silver lining was the forced break. For the next two weeks—one being in hospital—I was forced to recharge and heal. I binge watched TV, read books, slept and did a whole lot of nothing. It was the best thing for me.

Today self-care is part of my weekly routine. It's essential. And I've realised that self-care doesn't need to be yoga classes and meditation. It can be watching your favourite TV show for a couple of hours or going for a walk. Whatever makes you feel relaxed and takes your mind off things for a while. And it can be saying no to things and putting yourself first. I've realised you should never feel guilty about self-care. Taking care of your mental health is crucial.

Shortly after my hospital stay, I tried hypnotherapy with a psychologist. My friend, the one who had consoled me on Easter Sunday, had recommended it. She had found it invaluable during her infertility struggle and urged me to, "Just give it a try".

At my first session, I went deep. We were sitting in a small office, but it felt like I was in a huge school auditorium, with my psychologist (let's call her psychologist Morgan) miles away, her voice faintly echoing in the distance. Being new to it, at one stage I panicked. I couldn't wake myself up. Psychologist Morgan immediately spotted this and quickly brought me back. It was powerful. Another time I heard classical music playing. "I really like the music you played in our session". I had mused. "What music?" she replied, looking puzzled.

Ryan would often joke, "She's voodoo mind tricked you!" And while I wouldn't have quite put it that way, seeing psychologist Morgan was a turning point. Coupled with Cognitive Behavioural Therapy (CBT), the hypnotherapy helped a lot. CBT focuses on challenging and changing unhelpful thoughts, beliefs, attitudes and behaviours, and developing personal coping strategies that target solving current problems. You basically train yourself into positive thinking. One book I read at the time which I highly recommend is *Change your Thinking* by Dr Sarah Edelman. It includes practical and useful exercises on adopting the CBT techniques.

Using CBT, one of the first things psychologist Morgan taught me was to change my everyday language. Yes, each disappointment or set back was upsetting and often heartbreaking. It was normal to feel upset and angry, and it was important and healthy to acknowledge any pain. But she explained I needed to banish some of my language. Instead of using words like "devastating", "crushing" and "excruciating" or phrases like "this is the end up of the world" and "I won't be able to recover from this", she suggested I try phrases like, "I'm upset and disappointed this didn't work". She also recommended that instead of fixating on what I didn't have, to focus on what I did. The wonderful things in my life. And there were plenty of them. She encouraged me to try and not let the infertility consume me. Yes, it was a significant part of my life, but I shouldn't let it be my identity. I shouldn't let it have that power over me.

There is no question that adopting the CBT techniques helped to reshape my mindset and build my resilience. There were a handful of times, for example, when I started to have a panic attack on the train on my way home from work. This always seemed odd to me: Why would a train ride trigger a panic attack? But there I was, gazing out the window, listening to music and unwinding from the workday and suddenly out of nowhere, I would start to feel strange. I would zone in and out, my heart would race and I would feel lightheaded. And I was trapped. At least until the next station. So, in those moments, I tapped into CBT to help me through it. I would start by taking a few deep breaths in and out to regulate my heartbeat. I would then listen to a recording of one of my hypnotherapy sessions. And the panic attack would begin to fade.

Three months after the miscarriage and once I had fully recovered from pneumonia, we tried again. Given we had fallen pregnant on the last transfer cycle, we followed the same treatment plan but with some small tweaks to hopefully get us over the line. Dr Collins prescribed baby aspirin to stimulate my blood flow and Prednisolone, a steroid to suppress my immune system so that my body would be more receptive to receiving an embryo. I hated the steroids. The common side effects are irritability, anxiety and sleep disturbance. Just about three of the worse things you can experience when you're doing IVF. With an anxious, irritable and sleep deprived wife, poor Ryan walked on eggshells during this cycle.

The plan was simple. Ryan would take the call from our nurse, and he would tell me the result when I got home. It was the day before the Melbourne Cup (a public holiday in Melbourne) when we got the news. The office was quiet as most people had taken a long weekend. I was too impatient to wait. At lunch time, I went into a private meeting room, quietly closed the door and nervously called Ryan. He gently told me it had failed. I broke down. I was shocked. I had thought it had worked. IVF medication, especially the hormone progesterone, can trick your body into thinking it's pregnant. There is also an enhanced awareness of your body. You feel every twitch and twinge, no matter how small. You feel everything. For the past few days, I'd had nausea and dry retching. I thought this meant I was experiencing morning sickness, so I was convinced I was pregnant. I wasn't. Ryan left work straight away and came to pick me up.

On the car ride home, we barely spoke. That was it, I'd had enough. I'd heard people say that you 'just know' when you have had enough of something. I knew. I couldn't do it anymore. Something snapped in me that day.

As soon as we got home, I blurted out the one thing I was certain of, "I never want to try and get pregnant again myself. I can't go through this again". Ryan didn't seem surprised; I think he knew it was coming. He pulled me close to him and endearingly whispered, "Okay, we won't. You'll never have to go through this again. Let's try surrogacy".

As he held me and I soaked his shirt with my tears, an enormous weight lifted off my shoulders. I felt relieved. I would never have to go through this again. And with that, a sense of hope and even excitement started to sneak back in.

It was time to explore surrogacy.

CHAPTER 7: IT'S TIME TO GO ABROAD

Hope is a waking dream (Aristotle)

Surrogacy. Where to begin? Not surprisingly, surrogacy is an involved process. After attending a 'Families through Surrogacy' information evening in Melbourne and talking to Dr Collins, we decided to pursue surrogacy in Canada. Commercial surrogacy is banned in Canada, which leaves altruistic surrogacy. Altruistic surrogacy is where the surrogate has no financial gain for carrying a child. It's considered an altruistic gift. The intended parents cover the legal and medical expenses and the out-of-pocket costs like petrol and meals on treatment days.

From talking to surrogates, and from what I've read, they have been drawn to surrogacy after knowing someone who has struggled with infertility. They all have a story, whether it's a friend or family member, and it's a story that has stayed with them. And they've felt a strong sense of empathy to help. I think they're incredible and special women because most people have met someone who has struggled with infertility. But most women don't choose to be a surrogate.

So, what is a surrogate? I should start by saying that the technical term for our pregnancy was 'gestational carrier'. Surrogate rolls off the tongue better and most people know what a surrogate is, thanks to celebrities like Nicole Kidman, Elton John and Kim Kardashian. A traditional surrogate, however, is not only a carrier as she also uses her own eggs. Although these days, it's rare for that to happen. A gestational carrier on the other hand, is a woman who carries and delivers a child for another couple or person, known as the intended parent(s). But the carrier is either pregnant with the parent's genetic embryo, as was the case for us, or with a donor egg or embryo. Whenever I use the term 'gestational carrier', people get confused. So, for the purposes of this book, I'll use the term 'gestational surrogate' or 'surrogate'.

People often turn to surrogacy when pregnancy is extremely difficult or medically impossible and the risks are too dangerous for the intended mother. Or when a single male or male couple want to have a child.

To get started, we met with a surrogacy agency. In my experience, working with an agency is the best way to do it, especially if it's your first time because the agency helps you match with a surrogate and supports you throughout the entire process. This includes providing recommendations for fertility clinics, counsellors and lawyers.

The first step though was setting up our profile. Ryan and I submitted a bio of ourselves: "Happily married couple…we would love nothing more than a family to complete us", etc. We also sent in some happy snaps from our wedding day, holidays and family events. We needed to portray a devoted couple who would provide a safe and loving home for a child. Our profile would be the ultimate decider on whether a gestational surrogate even wanted to talk to us. First impressions meant everything.

Once our profile was live, the waiting begun. We had members' access to the agency matching site so we could see 'the competition'. Everyone had a sad story. I suppose that's the thing with surrogacy, it's often the last dance. There was not one couple or individual who deserved to be chosen over another. Many of the stories broke my heart. Most people had endured years of anguish and suffering.

In Canada, being altruistic, there is also a demand and supply issue. There are plenty of enthusiastic and desperate parents but only a handful of gestational surrogates. We were warned it could take up to two years to match with someone. "Two years! Do you think it will take that long?" I anxiously grilled Ryan one night. "I really hope not but who knows?" he shrugged. There was nothing he could say to reassure me. He didn't know. Neither of us did. There was no crystal ball for this one. We had to be patient and trust everything would work out okay.

We found the selection process straight forward. Once a gestational surrogate likes your profile, the agency arranges a Skype introduction. The surrogate interviews you as much as you interview her. Only two weeks after we posted our profile, we were contacted by a surrogate. I couldn't believe our luck. I had mentally prepared myself for at least six months of waiting. Nervously, we set up a Skype interview and prayed we would be a good match. We weren't. Differing personalities and views; I won't go into it except to say, we didn't feel confident.

A week later, another gestational surrogate emailed us. Her name was Julie. She sounded more promising and from our initial email exchange, I had a good feeling. We emailed back and forth one afternoon while she was at her son's karate class. By the time we Skyped, I felt I already knew her. My hunch didn't disappoint. We met with Julie, and her husband at the time, over Skype and we had an instant rapport. She had three beautiful children of her own, and she told us, "My children are my greatest blessing. I just couldn't imagine my life without them. I read your story and I felt compelled to help you".

It felt right this time. Once the call ended, we emailed the agency owner to say we were keen to match if Julie was. She was. It would be Julie's first time as a gestational surrogate.

It's difficult to describe the high I had that day. But it reminded me of when I was seventeen years old, excited and nervous about my first ever date and with a boy I really liked. I remember when I got home from the date, I couldn't sleep. I kept pounding the bed with my legs as I was full of adrenaline. That feeling doesn't come around too often, but we're all familiar with it. Nothing beats it.

Once the match was official, the paperwork started. There is an enormous amount of paperwork with gestational surrogacy including: child protection checks, police checks, consent forms, legal contracts, blood and urine tests for infectious diseases, and a physical medical exam. You are also required to undertake mandatory counselling and have a psychological evaluation.

Not being too keen on the counselling and evaluation, Ryan begrudgingly joined me on the Skype call. It wasn't like he had a choice. But to his surprise, he found the counsellor in Canada excellent. We both did. She soothed us with reassuring facts like, in her experience, "Ninety per cent of couples have success within two transfers using PGS embryos with a surrogate". And she always kept coming back to the one crucial point, "You have now removed the infertility". I found this reassuring as it meant we now had the same odds as fertile couples. Yes, it could take a couple of cycles, but there were now no infertility issues. And technically our chances were higher than the average fertile couple as we were transferring in genetically normal embryos.

I found Ryan's reaction to the psychological evaluation rather amusing. It was as if he had convinced himself that we were about to be interrogated by the fertility police and that unless we gave the perfect answers, we would be denied having a child. Of course, it didn't go that way. The counsellor asked us about our infertility journey and our understanding of surrogacy. We touched on our marriage and how we communicated as a couple, but the session was more an opportunity for her to explain surrogacy and set our expectations. It proved invaluable and despite Ryan's sweaty forehead and rapid breathing, we 'passed' with flying colours.

Next came the legal contract. This took a couple of months. Our lawyer was friendly and extremely knowledgeable. She made us feel secure and confident in the process. She also said, "You look like a young Meryl Streep. Why has no one ever told you that before?" Looking in the mirror, I could think of a few reasons, but I accepted the compliment.

The contract. It was like reading *War and Peace*. Everything you can—and can't—imagine was in there. One of the more obscure restrictions, for example, was no ice fishing during pregnancy! That clause always cracked me up.

Before you sign the contract, there are some significant points to discuss; for example, how many embryos do you transfer per cycle? Given a twin pregnancy poses a higher risk, most women prefer to do single transfers. As our embryos were PGS tested and therefore had a higher chance of implanting, we agreed that transferring one embryo was best. There are also decisions about genetic testing: do you undergo genetic testing, and if your baby is diagnosed with a severe disability before twelve weeks, do you continue with the pregnancy? And there are specific clauses about the intended parent(s): what happens if one or both parents die, or you divorce? Never pleasant things to talk about but necessary. Fortunately, all of this is balanced with some lighter decisions such as the birth plan and who cuts the umbilical cord.

Another important step in the process was organising the transport of our embryos from our clinic in Melbourne to Toronto. I didn't have the first clue how to do this but after speaking with our fertility clinic in Melbourne, I contacted a Canadian transport company who specialised in cryogenic shipping. The process turned out to be seemingly quite straight forward. There were some consent forms and then the transport coordinators at our Melbourne and Toronto clinics organised the logistics, e.g., when the shipping company could collect the container. To transport embryos, they are kept at a consistent temperature in cryo-storage tanks filled with liquid nitrogen. Transporting embryos is considered standard practice as many people ship their eggs, sperm or embryos when they change clinics or undergo international or interstate surrogacy.

Gestational surrogates have the same medical checks and psychological screening as the intended parent(s), but regardless of the results, you must trust this person one hundred per cent. You need to trust your gestational surrogate will follow the transfer cycle plan and take the correct medications at the right time; that they'll keep you updated on everything; and if they fall pregnant, that they will look after themselves and the baby. If trust is something you think you would struggle with, surrogacy may not be for you, as it's a long process from start to finish. A standard contract is approximately fifty pages and outlines requirements such as no drinking, drugs and smoking; maintaining a well-balanced diet; and no playing extreme sports (which includes no ice fishing, apparently). But there is no way to police this. I had read horror stories of intended parent(s) who lived in the same town as their surrogate, doing unexpected late-night drop ins to inspect their surrogate's pantry and fridge. Terrible! I'm not sure how that's legal.

One sticking point with Canada is that there is no pre-birth order. In other words, if the surrogate decides she wants to keep your baby, legally she can do this. Once your baby is born, you apply for parentage. But at the time of birth, the gestational surrogate is recognised as the legal parent, even if the baby is genetically yours. A terrifying thought. The gestational surrogate keeping the baby rarely happens, but it does happen. Of course, there are legal options, namely, the intended parent(s) can apply for legal parentage and pray that the court will honour the contract's intent and the DNA tests. But there are no guarantees.

Once the contract was complete, we were ready to start. We Skyped with a renowned fertility clinic in Toronto and met with a specialist, let's call him Dr Davis. He meticulously explained the treatment plan. Having been through several IVF transfers ourselves, we were already comfortable with the process, but we appreciated how he took his time on the call and never rushed us. After the appointment, Julie underwent her medical tests and checks. We were ready.

But there was one final step to take, working through the grief of not carrying our baby myself. When we first started trying for a family, gestational surrogacy was the last thing I ever expected. All I remember is feeling so excited, thinking a year from now, we'll have a baby. I'd bought some maternity clothes or clothes 'one size too big', downloaded pregnancy apps, bought the book *What to Expect When You're Expecting*, increased our health insurance coverage and booked an appointment with my gynaecologist.

When we fell pregnant the second time, I called the hospital the very next day. They confirmed my appointment with an obstetrician, booked a hospital tour and mailed me a welcome pack. And then we lost our baby. I abruptly tossed the hospital pack in the rubbish bin.

I now know that pregnancy is obviously not the most important part of having a child. Just as you don't get married to have a wedding, no one decides to start a family so they can be pregnant. I don't think so anyway! I can also recount several stories over the years from friends suffering debilitating morning sickness, back pain, insomnia...the list goes on and on. Most of my friends didn't experience the pregnancy glow often shown in the movies. And of course, the funny thing was, despite not being pregnant myself, I was very much part of the pregnancy process.

But having said all that, the grieving process was an important and crucial stage for me to work through. So how did I process the grief? What steps did I take? I started with having a few sessions with psychologist Morgan. I also spoke to other women, mainly through social media, who had had surrogate pregnancies. I found a real comfort in their stories. Many of them said to me, "Trust me, it won't matter once your baby is here. All you will feel is gratitude and happiness, not carrying your baby won't even cross your mind".

They were right. Yes, I did feel sad at times during our pregnancy about not carrying Spencer. I never got to feel him kick, I didn't get to feel him grow. But the day he was born and I held him in my arms, any sadness I was carrying melted away. Since the day I became a mum, I can honestly say I've never felt sad about not carrying him.

I once read though if you can't say to your friends and family that you're having a surrogate baby, it's probably not for you. You surrender all control, and trust with your heart and soul that this person will do the right thing by you and your baby. We trusted Julie from the start.

We flew to Toronto for the embryo transfer. Ryan's parents Kim and Steve excitedly dropped us off at the airport, their eyes full of hope. His beautiful nan Jean also called us the night before we left. One thing I've learned is that age is irrelevant when it comes to understanding infertility. A lot of people our age unfortunately just don't get it. Ryan's nan was in her late eighties then. I thought this meant she wouldn't quite understand infertility or surrogacy, which was fair enough. The first IVF baby was Louise Brown, born in 1978 in England. So, there was nothing even close to IVF when she was having children. But I was wrong. She understood. She greatly empathised. She had seen friends' grandchildren also battle infertility. She was, and still is, always loving and informed on the subject.

It was now April 2017. It was a long flight from Melbourne to Toronto, around eighteen hours (with a stopover in Los Angeles), but it was a huge milestone, and we were eager to meet

Julie and her family in person. With Ryan fast asleep beside me, I watched a marathon of pregnancy movies, starting with *What to Expect When You're Expecting*. I laughed, I cried and I started to visualise it all: How would we celebrate our news? Would I have a theme for my baby shower? What would the birth be like? I drifted in and out of a blissful pregnancy fog and it felt intoxicating.

About mid-flight, I couldn't help but overhear the conversation of the two men sitting next to me, "They're having heaps of trouble trying to have a baby". His friend replied, "Yeah, that's tough mate, we have friends in the same boat". The man continued, "But I just don't understand it, she's attractive, like really attractive. She's stunning. I wonder why it isn't working for them?" "Yeah, I agree that's really strange", his friend replied, looking puzzled.

That was the extent of their conversation. There was empathy in their voices, but my heart started to race, and I angrily thought to myself: She's really attractive. *Really?* What on earth does that have to do with anything? Like there's a link between the two!

It was one example of how much is still unknown about infertility. It wasn't the first, and I doubt it will be the last, ridiculous theory I'd heard.

Trying to shrug it off, I was itching to say something to them. But it was a long flight, and I didn't see the point. What would it achieve? They probably wouldn't understand and then we would all just sit there for hours in awkward silence.

I see the point now. And it's one of those moments I wish I could relive. Because education about infertility is so important. It's crucial. If more people speak up, there will be fewer of these ignorant comments and people struggling with infertility won't feel so alone, embarrassed, 'faulty' and guilty.

We arranged to meet Julie for dinner the night after we flew in. Having never been to Canada, we jumped on a 'hop on hop off' bus tour during the day and explored Toronto. We spent the afternoon at Ripley's Aquarium of Canada. We hadn't been to many aquariums before, but this one blew us away. Running around the aquarium like a couple of goofballs, our adrenalin was skyrocketing. We felt like kids, we were both so excited. Finally, this was it. Every time I stopped to think about it, my stomach would explode with butterflies. The transfer was tomorrow and a week from now, we could be pregnant. There was certainly a high chance of success. The success rate with PGS embryos and surrogacy is an impressive eighty per cent. By Christmas, we would probably have our precious baby in our arms.

That night we met Julie. She texted me an hour beforehand saying, "I'm so nervous to meet you!" I felt the same way. To meet the woman who was going to carry our cherished baby, how do you ever thank someone for that? I don't think they sell a 'Thanks for having our baby' Hallmark card.

We met at a restaurant in downtown Toronto, near our hotel. It had started to rain and only having a small flimsy umbrella, we got soaked on the way there. Well, half my hair did. Wanting to make a good impression, I had perfectly styled waves on one side and now there was a frizzy mess on the other. But that was the last thing that mattered. It had been six months since our Skype introduction, and we were so thrilled to meet Julie in person.

Within minutes, I spotted her warm smile. Walking through the loud and crowded restaurant, I nervously made my way towards her, but once Julie saw me, she ran up and hugged me tightly. It felt surreal and emotional meeting the woman who six months earlier didn't even know us but who now wanted to help give us the greatest gift of all, a child. Her (then) husband, her sister and her sister's husband also joined us for dinner. We talked for hours about everything and anything, from our childhoods and jobs to the local sports team. At one point I checked my watch and realised hours had gone by. It was just that kind of night. We eventually said our goodbyes as we would see each other again in the morning at the clinic.

Back at the hotel I could barely sleep. It was finally happening! I couldn't remember the last time I had felt so happy and excited. Yes, it had been a long, heartbreaking and sometimes scary path to get here, but we were finally here. We would finally have a baby and become a family. We had sacrificed so much, for years, but it had all been worth it.

CHAPTER 8: THE CANADA EVENT

History doesn't repeat itself, but it does rhyme (Mark Twain)

This was the hardest chapter for me to write. This chapter in our journey still haunts me.

We awoke early, eager for what was to come. The clinic was thirty minutes away, so we jumped in a cab and made sure we got there in plenty of time. Filled with nervous energy, my mind wouldn't stop racing. This was it. The day we had waited so long for. What we had fought so hard for. The start of something amazing.

When we arrived at the clinic, Julie and her then husband were already in the waiting room. We all anxiously hugged and checked in at reception. While we waited, we chatted about where to go for lunch after. "There's a Jamie Oliver restaurant not too far from here, maybe we can go there?" Julie suggested. It sounded perfect to us.

We continued to wait. Almost an hour later and Julie was busting to go to the bathroom. Having a half full bladder for the transfer, she prayed we would be called up next. As if hearing her bathroom cries, a nurse miraculously appeared and asked if Ryan and I could go to the back area to Dr Davis's office to meet with him first. "We would love to," I said.

Ryan looked nervous, fidgety. I couldn't understand why. "He just wants to meet us. Why are you so nervous?" I queried, somewhat annoyed at him. "Oh no reason, I'm just tired", he anxiously replied. Ryan would later tell me that he had a very uneasy feeling. He just couldn't understand why the doctor had insisted on meeting us.

Ten minutes later, Dr Davis came in. He slowly sat down behind his desk, and with a grave face he looked us both straight in the eyes and said, "I'm very sorry, but the container of embryos you transported over here is empty". That one word screamed in my head, it was palpable: *Empty.*

With a sudden pounding heart and almost breathless, I

asked him to explain what he meant, saying, "Empty? I'm sorry, I don't quite understand. What do you mean by empty?"

Calmly yet firmly, he repeated himself: "There were no embryos in the container you transported over here". Still confused, I continued to plead with Dr Davis, my voice starting to break, "Sorry, what? What do you mean? Where are they? Do you know where they are? Who can we call? There must be someone we can call?"

There was a look of pity in his eyes, a sadness in his voice as he said, "I'm so sorry, but you can't call anyone. There's no one to call. We opened the container an hour ago to start the thaw process, only to discover there were no embryos inside. We've never seen this happen before. I honestly don't know what's happened. The only thing I'm certain of is that your embryos have gone".

All gone. And that's how our day took an awful turn.

An hour earlier, we were full of hope and happiness. And now we were living our worst nightmare. Our embryos were gone. Our precious embryos, the only ones we had left. Any chance we had that day to get pregnant and have a baby, had been cruelly ripped away from us.

Julie and her then husband were sitting in the reception area, unaware of what was happening. It wasn't long before Dr Davis called them into his office to tell them. Julie's face turned ashen, and she burst into tears. She was as heartbroken and shocked as we were. Tears streamed down her face and like water from a tap, they didn't stop.

The four of us sat militantly in a row in front of Dr Davis's desk. I felt anchored to my chair; I couldn't move. I could barely breath. We all sat there in shock and despair. And confusion. We would later go on to learn that what happened was rare, extremely rare. When we spoke to our lawyers in Australia and Canada, neither of them had come across this before. Neither had our fertility clinics. Our lawyer in Canada did eventually dig up one case. A few years earlier in the UK. One case. There are hundreds of embryos, eggs and sperm transported around the world each week. She had found one case; ours was the second. I thought how the statistical chance of this happening would have to be less than one per cent. *Less than one per cent.*

We spent the next couple of hours at the clinic, desperately trying to work out what had happened. I think we spent four hours there, although the day is a blur. We talked around and around in circles, all of us trying to process what had happened. But no one had any answers that day and there was nothing anyone could do.

At one stage, Dr Davis and Julie left us alone in a meeting room. Once they left, I didn't know what to do. But I soon discovered that shock can have a profound impact. It was a warm sunny spring day, but I was freezing. I couldn't stop shaking. I had a sick feeling in my stomach that just wouldn't go. And there were times when everything went eerily quiet, as if I had lost my hearing. Above all else, my mind was racing, but I didn't have one clear thought. I kept yoyoing between what had happened and what we would do now. We had been preparing, for years, for this one moment and now it was gone. Unfairly ripped away from us. Our precious embryos were gone, taken away from us. They never even had a chance of a life with us. I kept thinking to myself: How could this happen? Will we ever have a family? Will we be able to collect more eggs? Or is this the end of the road for us? How will we be able to pick up the pieces and move forward this time? How's Ryan feeling?

To take a break from the incessant chatter in my head, I started to text a good friend about what had happened when I heard an unfamiliar sound. Searching the room, I saw Ryan. Hunched over, he was cradling his face in his hands and sobbing. I'll never forget that sound. And I'll never forget that image of Ryan. He looked so vulnerable. It broke my heart. Our dream was over.

Hours later, outside the clinic, we said our goodbyes to Julie. We were all still shaken and upset, but she remained optimistic and strong. "We'll make this happen" she said, squeezing my hands tightly and looking me straight in the eyes, "It isn't over yet, I want this for you guys more than ever now. We can't let this stop us.

Divine timing and all of that".

Julie has this saying, "Divine timing", that everything that happens in life occurs at precisely the right moment. Maybe this just wasn't our moment.

Julie could have easily backed away at this point. Heck, no one could blame her. But instead, she was more determined than ever. It was inspiring. "Maybe we don't have any more embryos," I whispered to Ryan, "But we still have Julie and that's really something".

We stumbled back to the hotel in the early afternoon. A few hours later (6:00 am in Melbourne), I called my parents. My mum answered and in a calm tone, I fought back tears while I blurted out, "I'm going to tell you something and it's going to upset you, but please know that we're doing okay, we'll be okay." I then quickly told her what had happened.

Taking a few moments to digest the news, she slowly started to say all the reassuring things parents say: "We love you. You'll get through this. You are both strong. You have each other".

My mum is the most selfless person I know. Always putting others before herself. Always. My sister takes after my mum. Two of the kindest and most empathic women I know. I could recount endless stories of when they have helped people, whether friends or strangers. Always doing it quietly. If I had not witnessed it firsthand as a family member, I would never have known.

And as a nurse, my sister always goes above and beyond what's expected with caring for her patients. Often staying back hours after a shift. Both Mum and Amy are warm and maternal. When I was at school, my friends would often say Mum was, "A milk and cookies" kind of Mum. Both my parents are maternal, and it's been beautiful to now watch them as grandparents.

When I spoke to Mum that day about what had happened, it didn't surprise me that she didn't get upset on the call and instead stayed strong for us. I knew why. She wouldn't have wanted to add to our grief. I don't know what happened next but being a parent now myself, I can guess. With a burning sore throat from holding back her tears, she would have hung up the phone and started sobbing. She would have woken up my dad and both being more emotionally outward people, they both would have cried, for most of the day. They wouldn't have been able to sleep that night. Or probably the night after. My parents and sister never told me how they reacted. But knowing them as I do, they would have been devastated. Ryan called his parents at the same time, in the hotel lobby. I imagine their reaction would have been similar. They would have been devastated. I know most of our friends cried when they found out. That was one of the hardest parts about what happened, how many people it upset. More than our hearts broke that day.

We had planned to spend a week in New York after Canada. We would have been in New York for the pregnancy results. Knowing that there was a high chance of a pregnancy, Ryan had secretly booked a surprise dinner and Broadway show at Time's Square. But now we just wanted to get home as fast as we could. I really hated that we were so far from home, separated from our family and good friends.

Before we could do anything else though, we had to cancel our New York airfare and accommodation and organise our flight home. Ryan is one of those rare people who never 'loses it'. I've always admired that about him. Throughout our entire relationship, I can count on one hand the number of times I've heard him raise his voice. Not yell, just raise his voice. I imagine that's some sort of record. Especially with the mountain of stress he was under with the infertility. He went to cancel our booking, but as it was less than 48 hours away, there was no refund. It was the final straw.

We were sitting on the edge of the bed when he suddenly yelled, "F&*k" and threw his mobile phone across the room. I jumped. He had taken me by complete surprise. It was the only time I had heard him yell. The only time I had seen him throw something. All his feelings exploding at once. I could hear the sorrow and anger in his voice. He was devastated. We both were.

I had packed some sleeping pills for the flight over. I decided to take one. I really wanted to shut my brain off and get some sleep. But it didn't work. My mind was racing too much.

I felt drugged but wide awake. A horrible feeling. We spent the whole day cooped up in the stuffy hotel room, tossing and turning in the bed, both crying on and off. In the evening, I thought we should get some fresh air. There was a movie theatre close by. For two hours, we could be distracted. It worked. We went to see the horror movie *Get Out*. Riveting and so far removed from reality, that for a couple of minutes at a time, I would forget what had happened. After the movie, we went to get some burgers for dinner. But with neither of us being hungry, we picked at our food and then headed back to the hotel. Back to bed.

We managed to book a last-minute flight for the following day. It was expensive and incredibly long, with a detour through Texas. But we were desperate to get home. We ended up being stuck at Texas airport for five hours and had a second stopover in Sydney. It took us one and a half days to get home. My parents picked us up from the airport. I could see on their faces they were emotionally drained, but they tried to keep an upbeat attitude.

That night, Ryan's parents came over. You could see they were both hurting. At one point, his mum rubbed my arm and apologised to me, a poignant ache in her voice and her eyes flushed with tears, saying, "I'm sorry, I know you're probably both exhausted and want to go to bed, but I needed to see Ryan. I really needed to see him".

I understood. She was his mum. The woman who had raised him. She never wanted to see her beautiful son hurting or struggling. She was heartbroken for him, for us. She needed to make sure he was okay. That we were both okay.

As we were meant to be in New York anyway, I spent the following week at home, alternating between the couch and bed. Ryan went back to work, always a good distraction for him during the more difficult times. Mum visited me each day and we tore through a season of *The Real Housewives of Beverley Hills*. Trashy reality TV was the perfect escape. The show was about as far removed from my life as you could get.

I also saw my GP the week we arrived home. I was in pain, an agony I had never experienced before. I couldn't stop crying. I couldn't sleep. I could barely eat. And I just couldn't stop thinking about it.

The main part I was struggling with was the unexpected. Like most people, I like predictability. I don't like being blindsided. With every other let down, whether it was a failed or cancelled cycle or even a miscarriage, we always knew it was a possibility. You mentally prepare, as much as you can, for the chance of it not working out. The unexpected nature of what had happened threw me into a tailspin. I couldn't begin to make sense of it. I was Alice down the rabbit hole.

I suppose that's the power of expectations. I had always pictured how I thought my life would be. I think most people do that. And this scenario was never what I pictured. So, when your life fails to meet your expectations, it can often extremely difficult to accept.

Throughout our entire infertility journey, this was undoubtedly my lowest point. I asked my GP if I could try a low dose of antidepressants. As I didn't have a history of depression, he swayed me against this. He explained that what we had gone through was a shock, a trauma, and I needed to feel it. I needed to work through the shock loss of our embryos, the loss of what could have been and the unfairness of it all. It could be worse later if I tried to numb the pain or bury the grief. But, if I were still feeling this sense of hopelessness in a week or two, we could talk about antidepressants then. He did agree not sleeping was "detrimental to my mental health" and he prescribed me some sleeping pills. I slowly started to catch up on sleep and with each day, I felt a little better, a little lighter. He was right. I just needed to feel it. The fog gradually started to lift.

It was also then that I grew a strange sense of superstition. For a brief time, I convinced myself that we were jinxed. The universe had spoken, and we weren't meant to have children. It wasn't in the cards for us. I couldn't explain why we had been inflicted with this bad karma, but I told Ryan one night, "I'm certain 'Someone' up there is against us. I'm not sure who 'someone' is, probably a higher being of sorts, but too much has gone wrong

Ryan and now this? How can something so rare and unlikely happen? I mean, how much 'bad luck' can we have?"

I continued to tell him that I felt like the universe had thrown a few curve balls at us, but we hadn't given up. We had even travelled overseas to get what we wanted. But there must be 'Someone' up there plotting and saying, "Time to take things up a notch. Surely some missing embryos will stop you".

I knew these were destructive thoughts. And certainly not helpful ones. Ryan, always level-headed, looked stunned when I told him. With a confused look he replied, "What you're saying is impossible, Kirst. And I'll be honest, you sound a bit ridiculous. I really think you need to talk to someone about this".

I went off to bed in a huff that night. He was probably right, but I was annoyed that he had dismissed my theory so quickly and I wasn't convinced that I was being ridiculous. This weird superstition continued to consume my thoughts for days. I felt angry at the universe. I felt cheated. But taking Ryan's advice, the next week I booked in a session with psychologist Morgan, and she quickly set me straight, "Remember, your thoughts and feelings have no bearing on the outcome".

It took a few sessions with psychologist Morgan for it to really sink in that 'Someone' wasn't out to get us. But soon enough, Ryan and I were back on track, as determined as ever.

Resilience is defined as, "The ability to be able to be happy, successful etc again after something difficult or bad has happened. It is the capacity to recover from difficult life events. It can often take time, strength and help from people around you".

Resilience, we would need it in spades. If the universe wanted a fight, it was going to get one.

CHAPTER 9: THE CANADA MYSTERY

Fall down seven times, get up eight (Japanese proverb)

What happened in Canada plagued us. We needed answers. The day we arrived home, Ryan and Dad called a senior lawyer with a credible reputation in medical negligence. Ryan also left voice message after voice message with our fertility clinic in Melbourne. But after not hearing back hours later, at night he furiously wrote an email to the CEO.

The next morning, the General Manager called him back. Ryan put her on speaker phone, and I could hear in her voice, she was rattled. She had read Ryan's email and had listened to his voice messages, but she was still lost for words. For any fertility clinic, Australia or worldwide, transporting embryos is considered common practice. She claimed this had never happened before and she was dumfounded as to what could have gone wrong. She asked us to meet at the clinic's corporate head office to talk about it further.

With multiple parties involved with shipping embryos, it was impossible to know who was at fault. But when we met with our fertility clinic, my blood was boiling. I suppose that's what often happens. You look for someone to blame. And out of everyone involved, the clinic was the one party we had dealt with the most over the years. The one party we were the most emotionally invested in.

From the moment we pulled up outside the head office, my heart was pounding. I couldn't stop thinking about the loss of our potential children. I also had a sinking feeling I couldn't shake: Is this the end of the road for us? To start with, we needed more embryos. All our precious embryos were gone. And while we had never had any issues with collecting eggs and making embryos, there are never any guarantees. Fertility is unpredictable. I thought to myself: What if the missing embryos were our last? If we do get more embryos and we transport them to Canada, 'what if' they go missing again? Yes, what happened was extremely rare. But once you know something rare is even possible, you add it to your list of possibilities.

And then of course, there was Julie. She had been determined to help us but 'what if' she changed her mind? No one would blame her. But then we would be back to square one. No embryos, no gestational surrogate. It was a lot of 'what if's', but I found it impossible to not worry about all the possibilities.

Our meeting was at 8:00 am as we wanted to get it over with. Ryan and I barely talked in the car on the way there, we were both so nervous and anxious about what was to come. All I could think was: Will we get the answers we so desperately want? Will we learn who was at fault? Will we have some closure? How will we feel in the meeting? How will we react?

When we arrived at the clinic's head office, we were led into a small unassuming meeting room. Ryan and I sat on one side of the table, and the General Manager and the head embryologist sat on the other. There was so much underlying tension but before the silence lingered for too long, the General Manager nervously spoke, "I'm so sorry about what happened. I'm sure it was very distressing. It was distressing for us to hear this".

She seemed sincere. But then it was straight down to business. It was obvious they wanted to prove their innocence. "Okay, let us step you through our process with handling and shipping embryos".

As she talked through their process, there were some noticeable gaps. Firstly, they couldn't confirm the temperature of the shipper once it had left their clinic (the temperature needs to stay at below -150 degrees when shipping embryos). A significant fact. While the temperature of a shipper is the responsibility of the transport company, the clinic had agreed to work with a company who didn't have an electronic data logger. In fact, they had recommended the transport company in the first place. We had trusted their recommendation, but the absence of a data logger was clearly a massive oversight. Also known as an electronic monitoring device, the logger tracks the inside temperature of the container (to ensure it stays below -150 degrees) and alerts the company if there are any issues.

But what really stood out to us was the lack of evidence that the embryos were even placed in the shipper to begin with. When we anxiously pressed them on this point, the General Manager firmly replied, "We can assure you that your embryos were placed in the shipper".

Whether this was true or not, not having any proof and simply having to 'take their word for it', wasn't good enough. We left the meeting feeling frustrated and angry. All I could think was: Do they really comprehend the magnitude of what has happened? Do they know these were the last of our precious embryos and possibly the only chance of us having a baby? Do they appreciate we have spent years struggling to get here? Do they really care…or is it simply a business to them?

The next party involved was the transport company. But being based in Toronto, it was difficult to reach them. We played phone tag and would annoyingly receive a call back at an ungodly hour, once we were fast asleep. We relied on email. But we soon discovered that while email is useful in getting things in writing, it's also a lot easier to ignore someone over email. The key issue with the transport company was the shipper containing our embryos didn't have a data logger. This meant they couldn't confirm it hadn't been x-rayed. If it had been x-rayed, our embryos would have been instantly destroyed. We continued to chase the company over email for confirmation that the shipper wasn't x-rayed. But instead, our emails were ignored—similar to our Melbourne clinic—and we received short replies stating they had followed the standard protocols. But there was no proof. Another dead end.

Still no answers. We felt like we were making no progress. We were spending lots of our time trying to work out what had happened and yet we were just as clueless as the day we had received the horrible news. No one seemed to know anything. It was incredibly frustrating. And the anger and sadness about what had happened stayed with us.

With our fertility clinic in Toronto, they didn't have any evidence the container was properly unpacked. But my instinct told me they weren't at fault. Yes, they could have been. But there was such an authentic look of shock and upset on their faces when they told us the news. It's also difficult to fathom that they could have lied straight to our faces. And we had spent hours at the clinic talking to them. If they were at fault, they should win some Emmy Awards for a very convincing performance.

Once we had spoken to all three parties and collected our 'evidence', we met with a lawyer. We liked her right away. Astute and knowledgeable, she greatly empathised with our situation, and took her time listening to us. She took us by surprise when she cited similar IVF cases, saying, "Regrettably, this isn't the first time I've heard of embryos being destroyed. I've worked on a handful of cases where embryos have been accidentally destroyed in clinic laboratories". She continued, "But your case is unique. I've never heard of any missing in transit".

As she spoke, I sadly thought to myself: Our case may be unique, but the outcome is still the same. There are other people who have unfairly and devastatingly lost their embryos, their potential children. For some, it may have been their final chance of ever having children.

She went on to explain that given there were multiple groups involved in transporting our embryos and all three parties had provided limited evidence, it was complicated. But that there were three likely scenarios:

1. There was a human error at our clinic in Melbourne when the container of embryos was packed.
2. 'Something' had gone wrong in transit with the transport company, e.g., the container was x-rayed, destroying the embryos.
3. There was a human error at our clinic in Canada when the container of embryos was unpacked. Ryan joked maybe what happened was like the scene in the movie *Ted 2*—Mark Walberg's character sneaks into a fertility clinic laboratory, accidentally crashing into shelves and destroying containers of sperm. Humour always made me feel a little better. Although I hoped he wasn't right.

We spent our time tirelessly investigating these three

avenues. But as our lawyer had warned us, it was difficult to prove negligence by anyone. All three parties provided what limited evidence they had and there was no clear guilty party. If anything, they spent half the time acting defensive and pointing the finger at each other.

I knew rationally what had happened was a gross mistake but, in my heart, it felt like an unforgivable error. Even still, after a few months of trying to solve this mystery, we stopped the fight. It was too difficult to find out the truth. It was an uphill battle. We needed to divert what little energy and focus we had back to our greatest fight, the fight for a family. To this day though I wonder, if we had found out who was at fault, would it have lessened our pain?

But our investigation wasn't for nothing. Our fertility clinic in Melbourne conducted a review of their processes with packing and transporting containers, and they made some adjustments. Interestingly, these changes included in future only working with transport companies who have an electronic data logger. If the temperature of a container drops or it's x-rayed in transit, they will now be able to detect where and how this happened. They also updated and simplified their patient consent forms (for transporting embryos). It was our hope that these improvements would help prevent this from ever happening to anyone else. I never wanted anyone to ever go through the agonising pain we had experienced.

A month after Canada, we were getting by. My depression had started to lift, but I wasn't happy. I was in a neutral yet fragile state. I burst into tears one night because the dishwasher stopped working. Yes, the dishwater. Ryan watched on in utter bewilderment while I hiccupped back a flurry of tears and yelled, "But why isn't the dishwasher working? What's wrong with it? I can't live with a broken dishwasher! How do we fix it?"

It was also at this time my dad started complaining of a constant pain on his right side. His doctor said it could be a few things: an infection, a gastro bug, a cyst. But given his age and to be on the safe side, his doctor ordered an x-ray. That afternoon, he asked Dad to come to his clinic immediately. The x-ray had shown a mass. A large one. There were also a couple of other smaller ones surrounding it. He admitted Dad to Emergency that night. Once there, the hospital began conducting tests and an oncologist was called in.

I'll never forget the phone call from my Mum. She told me that after reviewing Dad's x-rays and initial blood test results, the oncologist's diagnosis was cancer—probably non-Hodgkin Lymphoma. He would need to biopsy the masses to be certain though. The smaller masses could be benign or cancerous. If they were cancerous, then it had spread, and the prognosis would be bleak.

When I first spoke to Mum when she was at the hospital with Dad, she had been pragmatic and stoic. She said how at least they knew now what they were dealing with, and they could start to treat it. When she called me on her way home from the hospital, it was a different story. She was devastated. She couldn't stop crying and she sounded scared. For someone who's a fighter and rarely seems vulnerable, her reaction startled me. And in that moment, I knew it must be serious.

This news devastated me. My tank was running on empty and whatever usual reserves I had to draw on, had abandoned me. Dr Google didn't help. I spent the night visiting blog forums. But no one seems to share positive news on these forums, so I ended up reading numerous stories of people not recovering. Looking back over the past few years, I thought how horrible things can happen. This was another example.

I have always been close to my dad. You couldn't ask for a better dad, loving and supportive. He has helped me with so much in my life. I joke that he was my research assistant during my postgrad degree at university. He has always encouraged me to pursue my passions and has been there to listen and support me. I can talk to him for hours on end and confide in him about anything.

When he was diagnosed with cancer, picturing life without him was unbearable. I went to bed that night with a familiar sick feeling aching in my stomach. Unable to sleep, my whole childhood and my life with my dad consumed my thoughts.

Not to sound macabre, but I had assumed that because Dad was a male in his mid-seventies, cancer was most likely a death sentence.

But I was wrong. It's not always a death sentence. Non-Hodgkin's Lymphoma is a blood cancer that usually starts in a lymph node at one or more places in the body and can sometimes spread to other lymph tissue, particularly in the bone marrow and spleen, or to the lymph nodes in the liver. Dad was diagnosed with 'diffuse large B-cell', the most common type of non-Hodgkin Lymphoma. It is fast growing and aggressive, but it's treatable if caught early. And thanks to his doctor, they had caught it early. The other masses were benign; it hadn't spread. Dad has always been physically strong and so with everything he had, he fought it. He fought it hard. He underwent eight rounds of chemotherapy, which is always tough, especially when you are older. But he came out the other side and has now been in remission for over four years. It was a timely reminder that good things can happen at any time.

As we needed more embryos after the Canada incident, I did another egg collection. Despite the intense stress of the past few months with Canada and Dad's cancer diagnosis, I smashed my previous record. Seventeen eggs were retrieved; eight embryos made it to Day Five/blastocyst stage; and six embryos were graded 'genetically normal' after PGS testing. The myth about fertility and stress has always puzzled me. And well, it makes me angry. It's as absurd as the myth about stress and cancer. The two are not related. Some of the most highly strung and anxious people I've met have never battled a serious illness. While some of the calmest, most relaxed and most resilient people I know have battled infertility or cancer. And sadly, I even know a couple of women who have fought both. To be inflicted with both is unbelievably cruel and unfair. To these women, your bravery and resilience is inspiring.

Following the egg collection, we turned our minds back to surrogacy. We had three embryo transfers in the contract with Julie.

But we did a couple of things differently this time. We changed transport companies; that was a no brainer. And we didn't fly over for the transfer. We Skyped instead. The mere thought of jumping on a plane and going back to Toronto made my stomach turn. I knew I couldn't do it. And if anything went wrong this time, we would at least be home.

June, July and September 2017—all three transfers failed. I was shocked, especially given we had been told repeatedly by our specialists there was an eighty per cent chance each time. Eighty per cent and not one positive result. It didn't make sense to me. But while we found failed cycles painful, it didn't compare to the agony we had experienced when we had lost our precious embryos in Canada. So, while we were all really upset, we weren't devastated. We were mystified, though. With such high success rates with surrogacy and PGS embryos and no obvious complications with Julie, the negative results stumped us. Dr Davis couldn't explain it and he had no treatment options left for us to try. We had reached another dead end. It was once again time to move on.

CHAPTER 10: WELCOME TO THE UNITED STATES

Hope smiles from the threshold of the year to come, whispering 'it will be happier' (Alfred Tennyson)

"Ninety per cent of couples have success within two transfers using PGS embryos with a surrogate". That statistic had stayed with me. I first heard it from our counsellor in Canada. I later researched it and she was right. The ninety per cent didn't necessarily mean a live birth, but it did mean a pregnancy. If we hadn't even had an embryo start to implant within three transfer cycles, then it simply meant it wasn't working. Whether there was a reason with Julie we hadn't discovered yet or a compatibility issue, if it were meant to work, it would have by now.

With heavy hearts, we ended our surrogacy relationship with Julie. She understood. She wanted nothing more than to see us happy with a child. And if that meant we had to try something else with someone else, she was okay with that. "It's all about divine timing" as she would say. We will be forever grateful to Julie and how she tried selflessly to help us become a family.

Being scarred by Canada though, we turned to the United States. There was a big difference this time. Altruistic surrogacy in the U.S. is banned, which left us with only one option: commercial surrogacy. Unlike altruistic surrogacy, commercial surrogacy is an arrangement whereby the surrogate is compensated beyond just reimbursement of medical expenses.

The U.S. boasts the highest surrogacy success rates in the world, with a success rate of seventy-five per cent, compared to sixty-five per cent anywhere else. We found that extra ten per cent enticing. Ten per cent can often make all the difference. The other reassuring part about U.S. surrogacy is the pre-birth order. This means that your baby is legally recognised as yours at the time of conception. It's an agreement the surrogate and intended parent(s) sign before the child is born. You can file the order as soon as you have a positive pregnancy result.

Once we started to research it, we discovered that

surrogacy is not legal in all fifty U.S. states. Of the legal states, California is the most surrogate-friendly as the process is open to anyone, whether you're married or not married, a couple or single, heterosexual or LGBTQ+. For some U.S. states, while surrogacy is legal, it's disappointingly only available for heterosexual married couples. And then there are states like Arizona, Michigan and New York where surrogacy is banned. In Michigan, for example, the penalty is to up $US50,000 in fines and/or five years in jail. Who knew that trying to have a family would be considered a criminal offence?

Being commercial, it isn't cheap. The cost ranges from US$90,000-150,000. These costs cover: the surrogate's compensation (approx. $US30,000-38,000); health insurance; medical checks and psychological screening; legal fees; and IVF treatment and medication. And for couples travelling from overseas, there's also the airfares and accommodation expenses.

So why did we decide to pursue international surrogacy in the U.S. rather than in Australia? Approximately sixty surrogate babies are born each year in Australia; however, there are several hundred born overseas (ninety-two per cent of babies are born overseas and only eight per cent are born in Australia). Why? In short, Australia has extremely tight surrogacy laws. If you're caught engaging in a commercial arrangement, the penalty is severe as Australia has criminalised commercial surrogacy.

This leaves altruistic surrogacy, but the approval process is long and arduous. Intended parent(s) also need to find their own surrogate. There are no surrogacy agencies and it's illegal to advertise, so it can often take years to find someone.

There's also another roadblock. It's illegal in some Australian states to enter into a commercial arrangement overseas. According to the Australian Government 'Smart Traveller' website, "It is illegal for residents of the ACT, NSW and QLD to enter into a commercial surrogate arrangement overseas. Doing so could lead to arrest and jail in Australia". I've heard there are potential loopholes in the system to avoid this, but I'm unclear on what they are.

My heart breaks for people who don't have surrogacy as a choice, especially if it's their only option to have a family. And it makes me mad. It feels as if we're punishing people who can't fall pregnant. People who yearn for a family and are willing to do whatever it takes to have one. It's my personal view that we have an incredibly long way to go in Australia to rectify our surrogacy rules.

We were lucky we just happened to live in the Australian state of Victoria where international commercial surrogacy is legal. We carefully checked our finances one weekend and decided to push ahead. Yes, it was a lot of money but as one friend asked us, "What else would you spend your money on? An expensive car? A better house? Maybe some more holidays? All that s&*t means nothing. You can't put a price tag on having a family". He was right.

The other advantage with commercial surrogacy is suddenly the pool opens right up. There were no warnings about it taking one or two years to find a surrogate. Matches could happen as quickly as within a week. This was the experience of an acquaintance of ours who'd had twins born in Utah the year before. I spoke to her one night and heard about her "amazing experience". She gushed, "It was all so seamless! The U.S. is a step ahead of Australia with fertility treatment and Utah is a lovely and family orientated place. You'll have a family in no time if you choose to go to Utah".

Doing our due diligence though, I set up Skype meetings with agencies in four states: California, Oregon, Colorado and Utah. Agencies in the more populous states like California and Oregon were all bells and whistles. Impressive and with a solid record of delivery, but it felt like a business transaction, and this left us feeling uneasy. The elaborate slideshow presentations probably didn't help. We already knew from our experience with Julie that we wanted a genuine and on-going relationship with our gestational surrogate and her family. How could we not have a relationship with the woman and her family who were helping bring our child into the world? It felt cold and unnatural to not have this person in our lives.

When we Skyped with an agency based in Idaho, within minutes it felt like a chat with an old friend. No sales pitch, no slick PowerPoint presentation. It was a boutique agency called Rocky Mountain Surrogacy, and I could tell right away that the owner Tess was personally invested with all her surrogates and intended parent(s). She also told us how she'd had the unique experience of going through surrogacy herself, from both sides. She had been a surrogate for a couple and then later, an intended parent. So, it wasn't just a business to her, it was personal.

Within only an hour of meeting Tess, she set us up with a lawyer and a fertility clinic. The next day, she sent us profiles of two potential surrogates. The efficiency was astounding. For the first time in such a long time, there was no sitting around and waiting. And both the profiles looked promising. I can't remember what differentiated one from the other, but we went with a gut feel and we soon set up a meet and greet.

Given the time difference, it was 3:00 am in Utah. Leigha's husband Josh works shift work, so he wasn't home until late. Tess also sat in on the call. We felt awful about the ungodly hour, but they all insisted they were night owls. I can't describe how you can feel an instant connection with someone over Skype, let alone someone from halfway across the world, but that's what happened with us. I had an instant bond with our surrogate Leigha, and her husband Josh, and I just knew this was the woman I wanted to carry our baby. It was a gut feel. Like many people, I often have a sense about people when I first meet them. Whether it's their body language, eye contact, something they've said or haven't said. And that night, all I saw was a woman who was warm, empathic and considered. Funny and sensible. Easy going and intelligent. And I just knew, Leigha was perfect.

Ryan had been his usual courteous and friendly self on the call so I couldn't gauge what he was thinking. As soon as the call finished, I anxiously turned to him and prayed he felt the same way. He did. We contacted Tess straight away and then we waited. We didn't need to wait long. Within thirty minutes, Leigha sent us an image of a joey in a kangaroo's pouch and the words: "Ryan and Kirsten. I hope I can take some weight off your shoulders and bring you some joy in the years to come. I would be 'honoured' to carry your joey. Leigha." She would be honoured? We would be honoured too!

Given we knew what to expect this time, it didn't feel quite as daunting. As with Canada, there was an enormous amount of paperwork and the same medical tests. The contract was similar, but there were some notable differences with the legal process, mainly the pre-birth order. Along with our U.S. lawyer, we also engaged an Australian lawyer to check our contract met any Australian requirements.

It wasn't Leigha's first surrogacy experience either. A year earlier, she had given birth to a beautiful boy for a couple from Madrid, Spain. After the birth, they had lived with Leigha and Josh for two weeks before heading back home. Leigha sent us some photos from this time: from being at the hospital to family dinner togethers, you could see an abundance of love. The couple described Leigha to me as, "a sister and an American Aunt to our son". They were family. We wanted to experience the same.

The next step was meeting with our new fertility clinic. We Skyped with The Utah Fertility Center early one morning, and we were immediately impressed with our specialist Dr Russell A. Foulk and nurse Tonya.

We found Dr Foulk extremely knowledgeable and easy to talk to. He made us feel comfortable. As Ryan would say, "He seems like the kind of guy I could go out and have a beer with". But above all else, both Dr Foulk and Tonya were genuinely invested in us and determined to give us the family we so desperately wanted. Unlike most of our previous specialists, he acknowledged that it had been a long and difficult road for us. One thing I've learned is how powerful it is when people simply acknowledge what you're going through.

When it comes to regulation in the U.S., unlike Australia, clinics are required to annually publish their success rates. And there are some impressive success rates in the U.S. For the Utah Fertility Center, the live birth rate is approximately sixty per cent. In Australia, on average and of those who report their success rates, it's about half that. Sixty per cent—for the first time in a long time, the odds were strongly in our favour.

With surrogacy not being common in Australia, it's misunderstood. This made me nervous about telling people. What would their reactions be? Would people judge us? I've since learned that people will judge you no matter what, so it's best not to get too wrapped up in what people think. Always easier said than done, though.

Once everything was confirmed, we gradually started to tell people. For some people, their only reference point was *The Handmaid's Tale* (Season One had aired that year). They'd say, "Oh, so just like in *The Handmaid's Tale*?" Shudder. "Yes, just like that," I would sarcastically reply, fighting the urge to roll my eyes.

Most people we told had never met anyone who'd had a baby through gestational surrogacy. And then came the questions. So many questions. People were so curious about how it all worked. Fair enough. We had asked all the same questions ourselves. Predictably, some people—not any of our good friends or family mind you—asked some crazy questions. You could tell some people felt very awkward talking about it. Here's some of the more farfetched questions, and what I would have loved to have said in response:

1. **Wow, so the baby will be born in the United States. Do you think you will go over there once the baby is born?** No, we'll probably stay home and get the baby FedEx back, it will be cheaper that way.
2. **So....do you have to sleep with the surrogate (a male asked this question of Ryan)?** Of course, have you seen *The Handmaid's Tale*? It's just like that but without the fancy red robes.
3. **Are you allowed to choose the name?** No, I mean legally and genetically the baby will be ours, but we won't get to choose the name. Here's hoping the surrogate choses a cool name like Apple or North.
4. **Will the surrogate breastfeed?** Totally, refer to my earlier *Handmaid's Tale* response.

There is also the moral debate: What are the ethical and practical ramifications of women's bodies? Does surrogacy take advantage of poor and low-income women desperate for money; and what are the rights of the children born? This debate is often fuelled by the differences in commercial surrogacy between countries. In countries like the U.S., it's often a beautiful experience. Women who become surrogates are not driven by financial reasons. They are compassionate and empathetic women who want to help people become a family. I once read that it's usually two families coming together, forging a lifelong relationship, full of love and respect. I think this is true for many surrogates and intended parent(s).

In other countries however, like India, Thailand and Ukraine, it can be the stark opposite. The appeal for many parents is the competitive cost. Given the high cost of commercial surrogacy, I don't blame people for wanting to pursue a more affordable option. And don't get me wrong, it's not always a negative experience. I've read sincere and heartfelt stories from these countries. But I've also read awful stories of vulnerable women who are taken advantage of. Women who are financially struggling and would do anything to support their family, including having a baby for a stranger. Often several times over. Even when they are not physically ready yet to endure another pregnancy and birth. There are also horrible stories of how a baby is taken out of the surrogate's arms soon after birth and hurried off to a private room where the intended parent(s) are waiting, with the surrogate never meeting them or seeing the baby again. The thought of that makes me sick.

In 2019, there was a story on *Foreign Correspondent* (an Australian current affairs program) about commercial surrogacy in Ukraine, 'Damaged babies and broken hearts: Ukraine's commercial surrogacy industry leaves a trial of 'disasters''. The story acknowledged that while there are positive examples, there is also a dark and sinister side of surrogacy. In one story, the intended parents were deceived about the hospital standard (the hospital condition and level of care). When their baby was born, she required urgent specialised treatment, but they were subjected to a lengthy wait and horrendous hospital conditions. With the surrogates, the program showed many women living in poverty who were desperate for income. But instead of being treated as human beings, they were considered "a flow of incubators". I watched this story when Spencer was only two months old. Shocked and disgusted, I was so grateful we had pursued surrogacy in the U.S. This awful side of surrogacy was so far removed from our experience.

Not long after we confirmed everything with Leigha, I decided to Google the question, "Is surrogacy ethical?" I don't know what possessed me, probably curiosity, but as you can imagine, countless blog forum discussions and media articles came up. There are many people who are fiercely passionate, and opinionated, on this subject.

Here's a selection of some of the more upsetting headlines I read: Selling babies; Why surrogacy is oppression; Babies are tailor made to fit the desires of the world's rich; Surrogacy is a human rights violation; Surrogacy—a moral evil; International child trafficking; Surrogacy is a sin; and What surrogacy and prostitution have in common. So yes, it's a divisive topic.

For the next few weeks, the opinion articles and blog comments played heavily on my mind. One afternoon during another Google frenzy, I made a decision. Stop. I could waste my energy and emotions getting caught up in the moral debate about surrogacy or I could ignore it and focus on the positive experience ahead of us. Like so many things in life, there are always going to be firm beliefs and attitudes on human issues like surrogacy. In my heart, I knew there was nothing wrong or dishonest about what we were doing. If anything, it would be the opposite. For us, it was set to be an amazing and genuine experience. And one where we would hopefully forge a lifelong relationship with another beautiful family.

One thing I will say about online blog comments is while there are plenty of negative comments, there are far more positive ones. Towards the end of our journey, I discovered the amazing TTC (Trying To Conceive) community. From Instagram infertility advocates (myself now being one), to podcasts, fertility coaches and virtual fertility expos, there is so much support and so many resources now available. I found it so comforting being part of this community. It makes you feel less alone. And you also learn so much from each other.

There are also online fertility and IVF magazines and communities like IVF babble. The founders of IVF babble, Sara Marshall-Page and Tracey Bambrough, have done an amazing job at raising awareness about infertility and busting the stigma. As Sara often says about the TTC community with her former infertility battle, "I wish I'd had you lot when I was going through this".

Our first transfer with Leigha was in March 2018. For this cycle, Leigha had daily injections to control her menstrual cycle and prepare her uterus. She also had regular blood tests and ultrasounds to monitor her hormone levels and endometrium lining. Knowing firsthand how horrible the injections and medication could be, I admired Leigha's stoicism. Not once did she complain, or even briefly remark, about the medication or its nasty side effects. Not once.

We transferred a Grade A PGS embryo. The clinic impressively livestreamed the laboratory as they prepared for the transfer. Over a monitor, they showed us all the steps involved— identifying the correct container; opening the container; thawing the embryo; and gently placing it in the catheter. I thought how vital this process would have been in Canada. At the very least, it would have proven the innocence, or perhaps guilt, of the Toronto clinic. The same can be said for our Melbourne clinic if they had livestreamed or at least recorded the packing of the container.

The clinic was a two-hour drive from Leigha and Josh's home, up to three hours in traffic. Not that you would ever know it. Leigha never complained about the commute, or anything for that matter. Even when she had to go to the clinic for fifteen-minute appointments or had multiple appointments in one week, she always took it in her stride. In the U.S., bedrest is mandatory after a transfer. After all my transfers, I was back at work an hour later. With the U.S., they give you a Valium for the transfer to relax your uterus and then prescribe you two days bed rest. After the transfer, Leigha and Josh spent the weekend in a hotel near the clinic. And then the waiting begun.

Leigha was confident. With two boys of her own and a surrogate baby she had carried a year earlier, she was relaxed and optimistic. I, on the other hand, was a mess. I was petrified of another failure. It felt like the U.S. was our last hope. Having been through it all before, I found Leigha incredibly supportive. Leigha is a natural communicator so not a day went by when I didn't hear from her, often multiple times.

Ten days crawled by and then suddenly it was the night before the pregnancy blood test. Positive visualisation, meditation, and praying. I tried it all that night. But deep down I knew that however I felt, whatever I did at this point, it would not change the outcome. It never did.

We agreed that Leigha would take the call from the nurse and then she would contact us. Given the time difference, this would be in the early AM. We had agreed Leigha should be the one to hear the news first. Afterall, she was the one who was hopefully pregnant. And if it was good news, we liked the idea of hearing it from her. It would make it more special.

In the lead up to the result, Leigha told me about her positive pregnancy test with the Spanish couple. It was their first transfer. They were out for dinner when Leigha and Josh Skyped them to tell them the good news. They were ecstatic. Seeing all the commotion, the waiter hurried over to see if they needed anything. "We're celebrating! Can we please order a bottle of your finest champagne?" "What are you celebrating?" he had happily asked. "We're pregnant!!!" they squealed with delight. Giving the mum a judgemental and suspicious glance, he reluctantly went off to get the champagne. "I wonder how we'll celebrate?" I had eagerly asked Ryan.

Our call was different.

"I'm so sorry, I didn't want to be the one to tell you this,"

Leigha cried. The cycle had failed. We had been down this road so many times, but it was still immensely painful. It was the first failed cycle for Leigha, so I think it shocked and devastated her even more than us. You never forget your first failed one. It's the sobering realisation that IVF is not a guarantee. Along with the very uneasy feeling of: When will it work? Or will it ever work?

On her Facebook page that night, Leigha wrote, "I just can't understand it. I'm still in a bit of disbelief, it doesn't make sense".

It didn't make sense but then again, IVF rarely does. There's so much that is unknown. She ended her post with an inspiring quote: "Don't confuse your path with your destination. Just because it's stormy now, it doesn't mean that you aren't headed for sunshine (anonymous)".

Determined to move forward, I spoke to our nurse Tonya later that day and booked an appointment with Dr Foulk. Two days later, we Skyped with him at 9:00 pm U.S. time. Based on our previous experiences, I assumed he wouldn't have any insights or new treatments. I thought he would simply say to try again, that it was a numbers game. That was usually the line fertility specialists touted. I was wrong. Dr Foulk took his time on the call, listened to all our concerns, and then proposed something new. In the U.S., there is always something new to try. He recommended we do an Endometrial Receptivity Array (ERA). An ERA is a genetic test where they take a small sample of a woman's endometrial lining to identify the best day and time to transfer an embryo. Most women transfer five days after ovulation. He explained how twenty-five per cent of women transfer on the wrong day. It meant a month off treatment, but Dr Foulk assured us that transferring an embryo at the 'precise time' would maximise implantation.

For the ERA test, Leigha had a mock transfer cycle with all her regular medication, blood tests and scans. Dr Foulk then took a sample of her endometrium lining on the same day an embryo transfer would have occurred. I was quick to warn her beforehand, Paracetamol is mandatory! The sample was then sent to a laboratory to analyse the genes involved in receptivity.

I'll admit I was sceptical about the test, but I agreed it couldn't hurt. And it was only a month's break. A couple of weeks later the results came back. There are three potential outcomes with the ERA test: pre receptive, receptive, and post receptive. For most women, the optimum time to transfer an embryo is during the receptive phase, five days after ovulation. To our surprise, we had been transferring too early, during the pre-receptive phase. For our best chances of success, we would need to transfer twelve hours later. The time off and testing hadn't been in vain. We were now in the ideal position to make this work.

Ryan works for an international company and conveniently their annual strategy conference is held in May at their global office in the U.S. During May we had our break in treatment. Once the conference ended, Ryan flew to Salt Lake City for the weekend to meet Leigha and Josh and their two boys. As a sports buff, Ryan always tries to sneak in a game when he's overseas. The Utah Warriors rugby team happened to be playing that weekend. During the day, the five of them explored Salt Lake City before spending the evening at the rugby, bonding over the game, and getting to know each other.

After his visit, Leigha wrote on her Facebook page, "I can't put into words what an amazing day I had...I got to spend the day getting to know Ryan and a bit about his wife. So glad he got to spend the day with not only me but my family. I'm really looking forward to his next visit with his wife. Thank you for detouring to spend the day with us". Ryan didn't say too much when he returned home, but I know he felt the same way. His eyes lit up every time he spoke about his trip.

About three months after our first attempt, we geared up for transfer number two. We transferred during June 2018. We followed the same treatment plan but changed the time to twelve hours later. We transferred in a Grade B PGS embryo. An embryologist had told me once that there's little difference between a Grade A and B embryo. They are both considered high quality. I found this reassuring.

The next ten days crawled by and then once again it was

results day. It was early when Ryan got the call, around 5:30 am. Vigorously shaking my shoulders, he woke me up, yelling, "Kirst, Kirst, we're pregnant!!" Half asleep, I quickly shot up in bed. "Really?? Are we really?", I exclaimed, my eyes flushed with tears.

We were pregnant. Finally! Relief and joy consumed me. We Skyped Leigha and Josh right away and they were just as happy. As soon as we got off the call though, I had a pit in my stomach. I reminded myself it was early days. A lot could still go wrong. I shouldn't get too carried away. Had I learned nothing from the past? But I also knew the miscarriage rate with gestational surrogacy and a PGS embryo is half the typical miscarriage rate, so it's about seven per cent. Only seven per cent. That statistic calmed me right down. And like the Canadian counsellor had always said, we had removed the infertility.

A week later we had a standard follow up blood test to check the hCG was doubling every forty-eight hours and therefore the pregnancy was viable. It was. The hCG was high and rising. We started to plan. We knew it was premature, but we couldn't help ourselves. We were all so excited. We talked about our due date; the hospital; when we would be coming over and for how long; what the weather would be like, etc. You name it, we talked about it. On a call one night, Leigha and Josh invited us to stay with them at their home in Gunnison, Utah. We were humbled by their generosity, and we couldn't think of a better place to stay. After all, we were all in this together.

During week seven, we flew to Hong Kong for a mini break. We had already booked our trip before Leigha fell pregnant. But it would mean that our first scan, at almost eight weeks, would be mid-way through our holiday.

"What if it's bad news?" I had nervously asked Ryan. "It will ruin our holiday, we'll want to get home as quickly as possible" I said, memories of Canada flashing through my mind. "I'm not worried. Everything is going so smoothly and don't forget, Leigha's weekly hormone numbers are high. Don't look for reasons for it not to work, Kirsten. You need to stay positive," said Ryan.

Leigha wasn't worried either. Both Ryan and Leigha were

both calm and optimistic and that gave me some confidence.

With the time difference, the scan was at 3:00 am. That night, I told Ryan I was too scared to Skype in. I thought back to our missed miscarriage, and I didn't think I go could through it again. I was fortunate that I had a choice. So, we decided that Ryan would take the Skype call in the hotel lobby. The moment there was some news, he would text me and then I could join the call. But only if it was good news.

We went to bed at midnight. Ryan set his alarm to wake him up in three hours' time. Of course, I didn't sleep those three hours. I felt like I had drunk three strong expressos in a row. I was wide awake and jumpy.

At exactly 2:50 am, Ryan woke up, got dressed and made his way down to the lobby. I lay awake in bed, my entire body shivering. The first text I received from Ryan at 3:00 am was: "They're running behind with ultrasounds, she's still waiting". Ten minutes later, and riddled with anxiety, a follow up text: "She's going in now, it should only be a couple of minutes". My heart racing, those fifteen minutes felt unbearably long. And then his final text at 3:15 am: "Strong heartbeat, everything looks perfect".

A wave of relief washed over me. I bathed in those three precious words, "Everything looks perfect". I immediately jumped on the call and listened to the magical sound of our baby's strong heartbeat, happiness consuming me.

The next day we celebrated. We knew it was impulsive, but we were eight weeks pregnant and on holiday in Hong Kong. The scan had gone textbook. Her hormone levels were also high and the risk of miscarriage after seeing a foetal heartbeat had now dropped to four per cent. That night, we went on a boat cruise around Hong Kong harbour. Gazing at the light show as it illuminated the sky, a warm breeze on my neck, I felt so peaceful. At one point, I caught Ryan staring at me and beaming, "It's nice to see you so relaxed and calm Kirst". It had probably been a while since he had seen me that way. It had certainly been a while since I had felt that way.

For the next two weeks, we drifted by in a blissful fog. It

was finally happening. We were almost through the first trimester and by Christmas, we would have our beautiful baby.

With surrogacy, they schedule extra ultrasounds. Most women who are pregnant have one or two scans by thirteen weeks, but we had three booked in (weeks eight, ten and twelve). Our ten-week scan was once again at 3:00 am. Given everything was tracking along so well, we decided not to Skype in. Josh would film the scan and we would call them once we woke up.

I woke up at 6:00 am Saturday morning and checked my phone. Nothing. No messages. I immediately panicked. As Leigha is a natural communicator, I expected to wake up to a flurry of text messages and ultrasound photos. Ryan was fast asleep, his mobile on the bedside table. With a pounding heart, I checked his phone. There it was, a message on his mobile home screen from Josh: "I'm so sorry but we've lost the baby…". The rest of the text was cut off.

"We've lost the baby". The words screamed in my head: No!!! Not again!! Please God, don't let this happen again. We were so close this time. I beg you, please let this be a mistake. But even though I hadn't read Josh's full text message, I knew it was over.

Bursting into tears, I tried to unlock Ryan's phone but guessing his pin number, I locked it. Hearing all the noise, Ryan had started to wake up. "We've lost the baby," I cried. With a stunned look on his face, he grabbed his phone. We had to wait a minute for it to unlock before we could read the full message. One long agonising minute. We were staying with my parents at the time as we were renovating our house. Hearing all the commotion, they knocked on our bedroom door to check if everything was okay. I opened the door and collapsed into mum's arms while Ryan anxiously called Josh.

"When you hear the words 'there is no heartbeat' the trap door opens, and you fall" (author unknown). At the ten-week scan, our baby had already passed. Dr Foulk estimated that our baby had died at around nine weeks. Leigha and Josh were on their way to the hospital for a D&C procedure (Dilation and Curettage) when Ryan called. We were shattered. It was gut wrenching for all of us. It was Leigha's first miscarriage, so she was in shock. Our obstetrician Dr Adam Jensen later told us she is the only person he's ever known to have been crying so hard while the general anaesthetic was taking effect. He had tightly held her hand at the start of the D&C procedure and right up to the second before she fell asleep, she was sobbing.

I had previously read how surrogates are devastated by miscarriage. It wasn't only the loss of the baby, but it was also a sense of guilt, a feeling that they had let the intended parent(s) down. I knew Leigha felt this way. And that pained us. Of course, we knew this wasn't her fault. People can be in horrific car accidents or fall down a flight of stairs and the baby survives. Miscarriages are out of anyone's control. The hardest part of international surrogacy though is when something like this happens. All we wanted to do was see her and Josh in person. But we couldn't.

The rest of the day was a blur. At some point Ryan went off to choose carpet samples for our renovated house. It seemed like an unnecessary job to me, but he needed to do this to feel better. Distracting himself with tasks, whether it was work or our renovation, always helped Ryan cope. Work provided a sense of normalcy for him. From memory, I did the opposite. I spent the day crying in bed. I needed to release the grief and for me, crying always helped me heal. It was also comforting being in my parents' house, the home I grew up in. I have many happy memories growing up in my parent's home so whenever I'm there, it feels safe and happy, and like everything will work out okay in the end.

And that was exactly how I needed to feel as it was all over. Again. We would have to dig deep and find a way out of the darkness. Find a way to keep going, to pick up the pieces and move forward. I just wasn't sure if we would be able to this time. If I would be able to.

I was also so grateful for our nurse Tonya that day. She worked tirelessly with Josh to organise everything with the D&C procedure and to make sure Leigha was well supported. She also spoke to me several times throughout the day. At one point, I spoke to her for almost an hour before realising it was 9:30 pm

U.S. time.

There is always something incredibly special about nurses. This wasn't a job to her; you could tell she greatly empathised and was genuinely heartbroken for us. She wanted to help us through the grief. She also wanted us to have a baby and was determined to help us. She organised an appointment with Dr Foulk for later that week to discuss what had happened. For me, having the next step in place always helped me move forward. Organising appointments was always one of the very few things I felt was in our control.

The morning after the miscarriage, we Skyped with Leigha and Josh. Leigha was distraught. She couldn't stop crying on the call. Neither could I. I could hear the despair in her voice, and it broke me. I was so grateful that we talked as the first thing we got out of the way was that we didn't blame her for any of this. For twenty-four hours, she had been carrying that guilt around. She even admitted she had been scared to talk to us. She felt like she had failed us. Josh had to convince her to call us. I can only imagine what a terrible and heavy burden that would have been. The miscarriage also made me realise the significant commitment Leigha, and her family, were making.

Shortly after our miscarriage, I read an inspiring Instagram post by the actor James Van Der Beek. I loved the TV show *Dawson's Creek* as a teenager, although I'll admit I was more a Pacey fan. In his post, he was open and raw about the multiple miscarriages he and his wife had endured. But what really stood out was his refreshing and insightful take on the word miscarriage itself. He wrote, "First off—we need a new word for it. 'Miscarriage', in an insidious way, suggests fault of the mother—as if she dropped something, or failed to 'carry'. From what I've learned, in all but the most obvious, extreme cases, it has nothing to do with anything the mother did or didn't do. So, let's wipe all blame off the table before we even start".

I couldn't agree more.

CHAPTER 11: IT'S POSITIVE! AGAIN...

In the midst of winter, I found there was, within me, an invisible summer. And that makes me happy. For it says that no matter how hard the world pushes against me, within me, there's something stronger—something better, pushing right back. (Albert Camus, The Stranger)

For the next few weeks, we all got by as best we could. But what had happened was always lingering in the background, festering away. Ryan threw himself into work. I threw myself into research, determined to work out what had gone wrong. I was obsessed. I spent hours researching medical journals and articles. And perhaps visiting the occasional blog forum, which was never helpful, of course. Old habits die hard.

When I stopped to think about it though, I felt angry. And exhausted. I thought to myself: How are we back here again? This isn't fair! Will it ever be our turn? Like the both of us, Leigha was also gutted. She didn't sleep for five nights after the miscarriage. I knew that feeling all too well from 'The Canada Event' of not being able to switch your mind off. Your body is exhausted, but your mind is active. It's a horrible feeling. The night after the miscarriage, she had taken some mild sleeping pills, but they hadn't worked. She was eventually prescribed something stronger and then started to sleep again. With each day, she slowly felt better. We all did.

Once again, my friends came to the rescue. The day of the miscarriage, I had been too upset to call anyone, so I sent out a standard text message. I thought my friends would have been used to my 'bad news' texts but they were shocked. They had believed it was going to work this time. I received an endless stream of replies to my text, long messages full of love and support. One group of close friends delivered a large care package the next day, full of soul nourishing goodies like relaxation tea, chocolate, face masks, a candle, bath salts, etc. This kind and thoughtful gift was exactly what I needed.

Of course, the elephant in the room was: What on earth

happened? Skyping with Dr Foulk later that week, he had a couple of theories, but he needed to run some tests before he could be certain. The first test was a biopsy of the embryo. We received the results back within a week and it was a familiar tale. The embryo was genetically normal. We didn't find out the gender this time though. I had spent too much time with our last miscarriage imagining what life would have been like with a baby girl. It was heartbreaking knowing the gender, so I thought this time it was best not knowing.

The next test was a specialised genetic test. Known as balanced translocation, it's where a chromosome breaks and a portion of it reattaches to a different chromosome. In other words, sections of the two chromosomes have switched places. It's rare but in approximately four per cent of all couples with recurrent miscarriage, one or even both parents have a balanced translocation. It was an expensive test, but we had to know. A couple of weeks later, the results came back: It wasn't that either.

The final diagnosis was a Subchorionic haematoma. When reviewing the ultrasound images, Dr Foulk had spotted it. A Subchorionic haematoma is a blood clot that is formed by the abnormal collection of blood between the placenta and the wall of the uterus. It's really frustrating though as it can't be prevented or treated. The main symptom is bleeding. Many women who develop Subchorionic haematomas enjoy normal and healthy pregnancies. But occasionally, it can grow and can cause miscarriage, preterm labour or placental abruptions. In our case, the haematoma had grown, and it had cut off supply from the placenta to our baby.

I couldn't believe this was the cause. Of all things to happen. Most women who have Subchorionic haematoma are fine. I felt so angry that we weren't. I wanted to scream. Because we had been so close this time. So, freaking close. We had fallen pregnant, we knew our baby was genetically normal and Leigha had no fertility issues. My superstition crept back in—Was 'Someone' still out to get us?

Once we knew what had happened, we Skyped again with Dr Foulk. We had a laundry list of questions and he patiently replied to all of them. Even when I would sneakily ask the same question a different way. Although he always seemed to be straight onto my 'sleuth tactics' and would calmly, yet intently, reply, "As I said earlier, Kirsten…".

Our main questions for Dr Foulk were: "What is the likelihood of this happening again?"; "Can you talk us through your patients who have miscarried from a Subchorionic haematoma, and did they eventually conceive?"; and "Is there anything we can do to prevent it from happening again?"

He explained that in his experience, we couldn't prevent getting a haematoma and that in his opinion, the likelihood of having another one was higher than expected, around ten per cent. Many women have haematomas, but they don't realise as they don't bleed. Or maybe they spot a little and don't notice, so they never know. The chance of miscarrying from a haematoma is approximately twelve to seventeen per cent. But the chance of consecutive miscarriages from a Subchorionic haematoma is extremely low, approximately two per cent. In his opinion, he felt confident that Leigha would fall pregnant again and that she wouldn't miscarry from a haematoma. At the end of the call, he said how I should write a book and title it, *Stuck in Left Field*. We all had a much-needed laugh.

So, where to from here? I finally reached a point that I didn't think we would ever fall pregnant. With every set back, I always had faith. I was determined to fight. As the Japanese proverb goes, "Fall down seven times, get up eight". But this time, the fight had vanished. I felt defeated. The universe had won. I was struggling to move past the fact that we were here again. That the miscarriage was caused by: 'something rare'. Pregnancy of an Unknown Location; a thin endometrium lining; consecutive cancelled cycles; missing embryos; repeated failed surrogate transfers; and Subchorionic haematoma causing miscarriage. I'd quite frankly had a gut full of hearing all our specialists say, "This is rare". Was it rare? Or was it just not meant to be? Again, I started to picture our life without kids. How would the next five, ten, twenty, thirty years look? "Lots of sleep ins and awesome holidays, I suppose" I joked to Ryan one night. He didn't laugh.

To clear my head from it all, one weekend I meandered around our neighbourhood for hours. I started to cry as I grieved the picture in my head of being a mum. I let the tears fall, the grief pouring out of me. It was cathartic. I returned home feeling ready to close this chapter of our lives and move on. Enough was enough. But Ryan wasn't done. We had one last transfer cycle in the contract. We had a handful of good embryos left and Leigha was willing to try again. She was determined to see this through. From talking to Ryan and Leigha, I was on the fence. On the one hand, I didn't think it would work and after all these years, I was finally accepting that. But on the other hand, I knew Ryan desperately wanted to have one final try. Always pragmatic, Ryan reiterated everything Dr Foulk and Tonya had said to us.

We spent one night talking for hours. Ryan carefully stepped me through all the medical facts and statistics. And at the end of our chat, he tightly held my hands and pleaded with me to try one more time. "Just once more, Kirst, and then we'll be done. I promise. Please, I really think you'll regret it if we don't try one final time. We were so close the last time".

As he spoke, I reminded myself of how we had never given up. I was always proud of this. For years we had faced so much heartbreak, and endless setbacks, and yet through it all, we had kept preserving. And this pregnancy was the closest we had ever been to having a child.

Being a more private person than I am, Ryan rarely confided in anyone about what he was going through. I had a few close friends, some of whom had gone through infertility themselves, who I always turned to. It was a warm comfort knowing they were always there when I needed them. Surviving our journey would have been impossible without them. While Ryan and I would often talk to each other, I found that when you are both in the thick of it and experiencing the same pain, it's not always helpful. You can talk around in circles and sometimes even make each other feel worse. You often need someone else to speak to, someone who is removed from it. I'm so thankful Ryan had the loving support of his parents, brother and sister during this time.

Not long after our miscarriage, Ryan went away to the country one weekend with his sister Amy to visit their nan. And yes, besides sharing the same birthday, we both have younger sisters named Amy. With eight years between them, as her big brother, Ryan has often told me how he has always been protective of his younger sister, especially when they were growing up. Seeing his pain, she knew it was now her turn to be there for him. She later told me how they spent the night on their nan's veranda, drinking wine and reminiscing about their childhood but also talking candidly about everything he was going through.

That weekend, the last few years came storming back to Ryan. He opened up to Amy about how he was feeling, and she comforted him. Amy has always been a loving, kind and empathic person, and I was so grateful that Ryan had that time with her to properly grieve. He needed to grieve. They say silence only increases suffering. Ryan had suffered enough. It wasn't all tears though. At the end of the night, they raided their nan's pantry, stealing her beloved Kit Kat chocolate stash. Their poor nan awoke the next morning to find her lounge room littered with empty Kit Kat wrappers. I think it was a while until they were invited back again.

It was also during this time we revisited adoption. We had researched international adoption after the missing embryos in Canada and had attended an information session at the State Department of Human Services. The issue with international adoption, for Australians anyway, is that it is hard. It's bloody hard. There was only one country we qualified for, South Korea. For Chinese adoption, for example, there's a long list of eligibility criteria and the average waiting time is nine years.

While the process seemed convoluted, I must say the departmental staff and case workers were excellent. It's obvious that it's more than just a job to them. They are deeply passionate about helping children find safe and loving homes.

For South Korea, we met with a case worker for a preliminary interview. We were both working that day, but conveniently, the adoption office was only five minutes from my office building. I felt so nervous about the appointment. I wondered if we would be 'assessed' the moment we walked through the door, from our clothes to what we said or didn't say.

I didn't need to worry. We only sat in the reception area for five minutes and the moment the adoption case worker came out and greeted us with a warm handshake and a wide smile, I instantly felt at ease.

The appointment went for about an hour. It was natural and free flowing, and he told us he didn't see any red flags with us adopting. It was reassuring to hear.

But he also told us that the timeline from application to having an adopted child was three years but up to five years. And we would also have to cease all IVF and surrogacy treatment. On this one point, he had been blunt, saying, "You can't do both at the same time and hedge your bets. It's one or the other". But more than that, he said we needed to grieve the loss of not having a biological child.

My mum was adopted. She was raised by two loving parents, Joy and Graham. I was incredibly close to my grandparents. I take after them in many ways, especially my grandpa. I even look like him. I've always been a strong believer in nurture over nature because of this. I was heartbroken when they died. So, whether a baby was genetically ours didn't matter to me. Ryan hadn't had the same experience as me with adoption, but I could tell it didn't bother him either. I had read a quote once, "Family is not defined by our genes, it is built and maintained through love". Beautifully said. And true.

But we had left the appointment feeling deflated. What troubled us was the lengthy timeline, with no guarantees. It had already been almost six years and the thought that we could possibly only be halfway to 'maybe' having a child, was difficult to fathom. If we could try both surrogacy and adoption at the same time, that would be one thing. But we couldn't.

With all this in mind, we agreed to give surrogacy one last go, and then we would put it to bed and turn to adoption.

I'll admit I went into the final transfer half-heartedly. Yes, I wanted it to work, of course, but my thinking had shifted: It won't work and if by some miracle it does, then it will be a dream come true. But don't expect it to work as it probably won't. In hindsight, this was a defence mechanism. I didn't mean to sound pessimistic, but I had to protect myself. I didn't know how much more hurt I could withstand. I was struggling with the fact that even with me taken out of the equation, it still wasn't working. If it couldn't work with Leigha and PGS embryos, how could it ever work?

At the same time as our final transfer, I submitted our preliminary application for international adoption. I was keen to get the eighty-page form in. I knew that if we didn't fall pregnant on this last attempt, having the adoption in the works would help me heal and move on.

Leigha was more positive than me, but she was apprehensive. Her confidence had been shattered and she had her guard up. But guard up or no guard up, she defiantly charged into the final transfer cycle giving it her all. It reminded me of a quote from Atticus Finch from one of my favourite books *To Kill a Mockingbird*, "Real courage is when you know you're licked before you begin, but you begin anyway and see it through no matter what". I always admired Leigha's courage throughout our journey.

On 25 October 2018, we did our final transfer, our last hurrah. A few days after the transfer, Leigha felt sick. Really sick. She wasn't sure if this was a good thing or bad thing, but it reminded her of how she had felt when she was pregnant with her previous surrogate baby. A small glimmer of hope started to appear. I quickly brushed it aside though. I had learned my lesson too many times in the past. There was no point letting any hope sneak in.

Six days after the transfer though, she took a home pregnancy test (HPT). There was no denying it, there were two pink lines. I was at work when she sent through the photo. I turned to my manager to get a second opinion; in case I was seeing what I wanted to see. "Yep, there's definitely two lines there, Kirst!" he said with a wide smile.

We had been told many times throughout the years to

never rely on HPTs. They are not always accurate. I had heard this on countless occasions. Many of our nurses throughout the years told us, "The blood test is the only reliable result. The HPT will show that you're pregnant, but it won't show whether the pregnancy is viable".

I thought back to when we had the 'Pregnancy of an Unknown Location'. There had been two lines on that HPT as well. But this time was different. With each day, the line gradually got darker and suddenly that small glimmer of hope I had pushed aside, made its way out of the shadows. It was a tantalising glimpse into what could be. Conveniently, the blood test result was Tuesday 6 November, Melbourne Cup Day, a public holiday (Yes, we get a day off in Melbourne for a horse race, albeit a famous one!). With Tonya away that day, we had been told that another nurse would contact Leigha.

When I woke up Tuesday morning, there was no call or text from Leigha. It was 4:00 pm in the U.S. I turned to Ryan, a pang of anxiety in my stomach, saying, "We should know by now". I messaged Leigha right away. She hadn't heard anything either. We had accidentally been told, somewhere along the way, the nurses first call their patients who have a positive result. That way, they have more time in the afternoon to spend with the people who received a negative one. We agreed that not hearing anything yet was a bad sign.

To distract myself, I checked my emails. There it was. An email from one of the nurses had been sitting there for more than three hours with the subject line 'GC Update'. We had never expected an email, so I hadn't thought to check. The email simply said: "Hello Kirsten. We received Leigha's results back today, and they came back positive!!! We like to see hCG around 50-100 and hers came back 297! This is a wonderful start!!!"

"This is a wonderful start!!!" It *was* a wonderful start. And this time it felt different. Now that we were pregnant, I was more confident than I'd previously been. One thing that I had always in the back of my mind from the start of our surrogacy journey, was whether there was a genetic abnormality we hadn't discovered yet. Perhaps something rare. It would certainly explain the failed surrogacy cycles in Canada. But the specialised genetic testing from our last miscarriage had finally put my mind at ease. So, here we were. A perfect embryo, a thick healthy endometrium lining and an extremely small chance of a recurring haematoma causing miscarriage.

In reverse, Ryan and Leigha, who had both been optimistic and confident the last time, were cautious and nervous. That excited adrenalin they radiated with during our previous pregnancy had gone. They were happy, of course, but it was different. They were "cautiously optimistic" as Ryan put it. Ryan was also adamant that we weren't to tell anyone about the pregnancy until at least twelve weeks. He only wanted our parents to know. I agreed, but I may have quietly told my sister and a couple of close friends. As my unofficial group of counsellors and cheer leaders, I relied on their daily reassurance that everything would work out this time.

At eight weeks pregnant on 1 December 2018, we had our first scan. Like our last pregnancy, everything looked perfect, and the heartbeat was strong. But there it was, another Subchorionic haematoma. A small black mass staring back at us. We couldn't believe it. The sonographer immediately noticed our panic and tried to reassure us. She told us that unlike last time, this haematoma was tiny and in a much better position. It was nowhere near the placenta. They would keep a close eye on it, but it was 'unlikely' that it would cause any issues. If anything, it would probably just resolve itself, in time. We had to trust that everything would be okay. "Always easier said than done", I muttered, "Especially with our fabulous track record".

We all felt so worried about the haematoma. It made it impossible to enjoy the pregnancy at this point. Leigha felt uneasy nearly every day, so we booked in extra ultrasounds and blood tests. Ryan made sure we Skyped in for every scan, every appointment, no matter how short or long, no matter the time. Missing the scan over Skype when we had the miscarriage, is still one of his biggest regrets.

At nine weeks pregnant on 9 December, we had an

ultrasound at 4:00 am. It was the same night as my work Christmas party. The theme of the party was masquerade, which was quite fitting. I spent the night smiling, laughing and socialising with work colleagues, while carefully hiding my true emotions behind my mask. It was a mask I had worn many times throughout the years.

As we had lost our previous baby at nine weeks, I felt particularly nervous about this scan. When I arrived home from the party around midnight, my mask abruptly came off and my old nemesis, anxiety, paid me a visit. We set our alarm for 3:50 am and went to bed. I think I did fall asleep for about an hour or so. And I knew I had to Skype in this time. Good or bad news, I couldn't sit this one out. Leigha agreed but she asked if her and Josh could start the appointment without us. As soon as there was good news, she would call us. But if it was bad news, she preferred to have a minute to let it digest before we joined the call. I completely understood.

At 4:05 am, she Skyped us. That precious sound, the heartbeat, was strong and healthy. My anxiety melted away and all I felt was relief and happiness.

A week later on 15 December we had our ten-week ultrasound. Another strong heartbeat: our baby was flourishing. It was also our first scan where the baby was active. For the week that followed, I would often catch Ryan secretly viewing the video and laughing each time the sonographer said, "The baby's turning now to say hello".

We continued to have weekly ultrasounds. Besides alleviating any anxiety, we also had multiple scans to check the haematoma. It remained small and in a good position, far away from the placenta.

It was now late December 2018 and almost time for our twelve-week scan. We knew that if everything went well at this scan, the risk of miscarriage dropped to only two per cent. Or as I liked to think of it, the chance of us finally having a baby was ninety-eight per cent.

After our last miscarriage, we needed something to take

us out of our slump, so we had booked a Christmas holiday to Europe. It felt impulsive at the time, but that also made it enticing and something to look forward to. But there was one problem. Our twelve-week scan was on 29 December, the night we were due to fly out. So much for never missing a scan again. There was a three-hour stopover in Singapore and then the appointment would be one hour after we left Singapore. One hour. I couldn't believe the timing. It was then a further thirteen-hour flight, so when we landed, the scan would have been twelve hours earlier. I checked with the airline and there was no Wi Fi on the flight. We would have to be patient and wait it out, our speciality.

As you can probably guess, the time felt long, agonisingly long. There are only so many inflight movies you can watch to distract yourself. Once we started to descend, Ryan suggested, "I think it's best if we wait until we get off the flight to find out the news. We can find a quiet spot somewhere?" An almost impossible task at Heathrow airport! I abruptly cut him off, "You've got to joking right?" I couldn't wait, especially as the time to get off an international flight can often be thirty minutes or more. He reluctantly agreed. As soon as we landed, I grabbed the sick bag while Ryan nervously turned on his phone. Straight away, his home screen filled with an ultrasound photo of our baby and the words, "Your baby is perfect".

We both burst into tears. Truth be told, we jumped up and down, squealed and hugged each other. Our fellow passengers looked at us like we were nuts. But we didn't care. We were so incredibly happy. I had also never felt so energised after such a long flight.

Talking incessantly as we made our way through Heathrow airport, we called our parents. They obviously knew about the pregnancy, but they had been on tenterhooks waiting to hear how the scan went.

After we spoke to our parents, I was waiting outside the airport bathroom for Ryan when I decided to text a good friend about our news. She wrote back straight away, "Well, it looks like Baby McWilson will have a play mate, we're seven weeks pregnant!

We had our first scan yesterday and everything looks great". It was her third child. I had to pinch myself. I was convinced all my close friends had finished having children. When Ryan came back out, he found me jumping around with excitement as I told him. It was an amazing feeling. A few weeks on, another close friend, the one who had previously lived in Germany, called me one afternoon to say, "Good things happen in threes, I'm pregnant as well". She was also pregnant with her third child. I couldn't believe it.

Years earlier, at the same time as us, many of my good friends were trying, and succeeding, to fall pregnant. I had always been excited by the idea of pushing our prams together, having play dates, swapping our sleep deprived stories, etc. One by one they fell pregnant with their firsts, and then their second babies, while I watched the door on sharing this beautiful and special experience with them slowly close. But now the door was open again. Two of my best friends, both of whom had been my bridesmaids, were pregnant. It had been what I had dreamed of for years.

CHAPTER 12: SPENCER

It always seems impossible until it's done (Nelson Mandela)

We arrived home from Europe on 19 January 2019, at fifteen weeks pregnant. In the U.S., it's popular to find out the gender of your baby through gender reveal parties and cakes. People go all out. In Arizona in 2018, one 'overly enthusiastic' Dad caused a wildfire. He shot a makeshift target that had the words 'Boy' and 'Girl' written on it. The target had exploded and revealed a blue cloud. And then the flames spread. The fire burned 47,000 acres and caused more than $US8 million in damage. Like I said, people go all out.

In recent years, it's become quite popular in Australia as well. As we needed to know the gender to complete the pre-birth order, the day after we arrived home from Europe, Josh surprised us with a gender reveal cake. Our parents and my sister joined us, and we Skyped in Leigha and Josh. It took Ryan a few tries to cut through the thick icing, but it wasn't too long until we all saw blue.

I didn't care about gender. Ryan was the same. Anyone struggling with infertility will agree. You never have a gender preference; the preference is to have a baby. But finding out we were having a boy did make it feel more real. With each scan, we started to say 'he'. We also started to 'debate' baby names. We had chosen a girl's name about four years earlier. One night watching a movie together, we loved the name of one of the characters. Even though this character turned out to a psychotic murderer, we found her name, 'India', really pretty. But we found choosing a boy's name much more difficult. In my lunch hour at work one day, I scrolled through a list of 1,000 boy names (there are some bizarre names out there, by the way). I then sent Ryan a 'short list' of twenty boy names. He politely pointed out that twenty names wasn't a short list. But there were three names he loved; Spencer was one of them.

In May, Ryan's annual conference in the U.S. came around again and the timing could not have been more perfect. He would be in the U.S. when our baby was thirty weeks, so he could do a quick detour to Utah and be there for a thirty-week scan. It took about thirty minutes, and it felt strange watching the scan at home alone, with Ryan on the other side of the screen. But I know he really treasured that moment.

I was jealous. I would have given anything to go. And even though I Skyped in, I felt like a bystander, a third wheel. Someone who had nothing useful to contribute. Did I even need to Skype in?

No one made me feel this way, of course. Ryan, Leigha, Josh and the sonographer constantly engaged me and asked me questions. But it didn't change the fact that Ryan was finally in the same room as our son, and I was miles away.

When Ryan arrived home, he told me it had been an amazing trip. Visiting Leigha and Josh's hometown Gunnison, meeting our obstetrician, touring the hospital and most of all, being there in person for the scan. He also got to feel a few kicks. He nervously asked Leigha one night, "Is it okay if I feel him kick?". He wanted to make sure it was 'appropriate' to touch her pregnant belly. Leigha had laughed at him. "Of course, it is! It's your baby! You can feel your son kick as often as you would like".

I had been warned by our fertility counsellors in Canada and the U.S. about feeling jealous. Whether it was Leigha's growing belly or Ryan feeling a kick during his visit, I may be resentful that I wasn't the one who was carrying him. I'm relieved to say I never felt this way.

There were a few things that surprised me about myself along our journey and this was one of them. Early on in our infertility journey, I had felt jealous of friends being pregnant. I was even jealous of women on the street being pregnant. I would often walk past a woman on the street pushing a pram, see a wedding ring on her finger and bitterly think to myself: Wow, she really has it all. Lucky her. I hope she appreciates what she has. But you never really know a person's story. I now wonder if anyone suffering infertility has walked past me on the street, as I'm pushing Spencer in the pram while he laughs and claps and I have a wide smile on my face, internally feeling so grateful. What would the woman on the street suffering infertility think? Would she think to herself: She has a lot to smile about, but I bet she doesn't know just how lucky she is?

I often reflect on this. One of the silver linings of infertility, of fighting any battle, is you try to stop making assumptions about people. Just because someone seems happy on the outside, and appears to have the perfect life, it doesn't mean they do. They could be carrying a suffering you know nothing about.

Jealousy. It's a rotten emotion. But one that's universal. There's not a person alive who hasn't experienced jealousy at some point in their life. Given my past feelings with friends being pregnant or strangers on the street being pregnant, I had assumed I would feel jealous when Leigha was pregnant. But I didn't. Why? Well, right before we fell pregnant, I had grieved the loss of ever having children. The last thread of hope I had had was gone. So, once we were past twelve weeks, I couldn't care less if I were the one who was pregnant or not. We were finally having a baby, that was all that mattered.

The other powerful reason though was Leigha. She always used inclusive language like "we"; I often felt like I was the one carrying him. And she would say she was, "extreme babysitting" or that she had a "hitchhiker on board". One day I mustered up the courage to ask her if she had felt attached to her other surrogate baby once he was born. No, she hadn't. She said she never saw it that way. He was never hers to begin with. She had no genetic connection to him. She had gone into surrogacy with that mindset. She said she felt similar when a good friend or a sibling has a baby. Love and happiness but nothing more. If anything, she said she was much more upset saying goodbye to his parents.

Our due date was 12 July 2019, the same day as my dad's birthday. We had planned to fly to the U.S. on 28 June, two weeks beforehand. On 19 June at thirty-six weeks, Leigha experienced some mild Braxton Hicks contractions. Often known as false labour pains, they are contractions of your uterus in preparation for giving birth. Leigha had gone in for her weekly nonstress test to check the baby was doing well and getting enough oxygen. All her readings were fine, but there were a lot of Braxton Hicks contractions showing up on the test. Only, they weren't Braxton Hicks.

I had just started my maternity leave when Leigha called. I

had planned to have two weeks at home to finish off the nursery, host a baby shower, organise our trip over, etc. The usual stuff. In a panic, Leigha told me she was having contractions, real ones, and had started dilatating. According to our obstetrician Dr Jensen, this meant she could have the baby any time: "It could be tomorrow or a week from now". He went on to say that while some people can have contractions for weeks, most people have them twenty-four to forty-eight hours before giving birth, which was Leigha's typical experience. It was a lot of information to take in. And the only certainty was, there was no way of knowing. With everything we had gone through to get here though, we didn't want to take any chances. We jumped on a flight the next day.

It was a comedy of errors the day we left. A rainy winter's day, overnight our roof had leaked. There was water everywhere. Ryan frantically went into work to finish up and say goodbye to his team, originally thinking he had two weeks left. I called an emergency plumber and started to pack in a panic, doing load after load of laundry.

My mum was coming with us. I couldn't imagine this experience without her. She had to be there. Being close to my parents, I wanted them both there. Dad was sadly too sick to travel, but Mum was coming and frantically packing. Except she had to pack using a torch as the power at their place had gone out. On a dark winter's day, no less. But despite all of this, we were so relieved we were able to change our flight at the last minute. We left Melbourne on a cold rainy night and arrived in Utah on a beautiful summer's evening.

Josh picked us up from the airport. As Josh and Ryan had already met twice before, they greeted each other like old friends. Mum and I nervously hugged Josh, but it wasn't long before we felt just as comfortable. The drive from Salt Lake City to their hometown Gunnison was three hours. I sat in the back of Josh's truck, reflecting on the past six years, and picturing the moment I would meet Leigha in person.

We pulled up to their house around midnight. Stepping out of the truck, the second I caught a glimpse of Leigha's warm infectious smile, I turned to mush and was a babbling mess. We hugged each other so tightly, both crying. Seeing Leigha in person, and with her pregnant belly, made me feel so emotional. He was in there. After all this time, I was finally in the same room as my son.

We spent the next few hours chatting on their couch. Two of the most genuine and decent people you will ever meet, Leigha and Josh made us feel so welcome. For the next few weeks, their home was our home. That night I also got to feel Spencer kick. Throughout the pregnancy, Leigha sent me random boxing emojis. Feeling her belly, I finally understood why. She joked that he had kicked her so hard once, she was scared he may have broken her ribs. Although once I felt him karate kick for myself, I wasn't sure she was joking.

So, of course, nothing went according to my plan. We were all convinced that Spencer would be born at any moment. We packed our hospital bags, assembled the car seat and pram and then the waiting begun. But he wasn't ready to come out just yet. At every appointment, Leigha was more and more dilated. Dr Jensen would say to us, "Any day now, I wouldn't be surprised if he's born in the next day or two".

This went on for two weeks. It ended up being a blessing though. During that time, we met Leigha and Josh's close friends and family and explored Gunnison. A gorgeous warm summer, we spent our days swimming at the nearby lake, and driving up the mountains. We also went for several long walks in Palisades State Park in the hope of inducing labour. At night, we watched movies together or played table tennis which, as it turns out, can be quite the challenging game! I may have been embarrassingly beaten, nearly every time, by their two sons.

At thirty-nine weeks, Dr Jensen recommended we have Leigha induced. We were due at the hospital at 6:00 pm on Friday 5 July. The day before it was Thursday 4 July. I'd seen the Fourth of July in movies and often wondered what it would be like. It certainly lived up to the hype. If there is one thing you can say about Americans, it's that they're patriotic. In the lead up to the Fourth of July, the town was blanketed in red, white and blue. Every house proudly had an American flag hoisted on their front lawn. There is also something rather special and charming about a small town. There's a real sense of community and family. Gunnison has a population of approximately 4,000 and it's a beautiful town, surrounded by spectacular canyons and mountains. Strolling through the Fourth of July festival in the park, many people stopped to say hi to Leigha and Josh. The highlight though was the fireworks. In Utah, residential fireworks are legal from 2-5 July. And let's just say that residential fireworks in the U.S. are big and loud, what would be considered commercial grade in Australia. Everyone loved them, except maybe their dogs. That night, we went to bed with the surreal feeling that when we woke up, it would be the day our son would be born.

But nothing goes according to plan. At around 2:30 am, I heard some commotion outside our bedroom door. Half asleep, I stumbled out to see Leigha leaning on the wall trying to hold herself up, crouched over and moaning. Josh was running around getting her hospital bag and locking up the house. It was time. We had been through this scenario a million times but even still, Ryan and I both froze. "Do you think I have time to have a quick shower?" I innocently asked Ryan. He shot me a you've-got-to-be-kidding-me! look. No, there wasn't time. Thankfully, Josh took charge and led the way. Formerly a Marine, Josh has a strong sense of order, efficiency, and calmness about him. We grabbed our bags, woke up Mum and jumped in the car.

Rushing through the hospital doors, on arrival we were treated like celebrities. The hospital staff were so excited for us, with many of the nurses requesting to work the shift. It was only the second surrogate baby for the hospital and town; the first was Leigha's other surrogate baby a couple of years earlier. Making our way to the birthing suite, many of the nurses stopped to give me a hug and say how happy they were for us. They even kindly organised our own private room, right next to Leigha's.

For the next couple of hours, Leigha had contractions but suddenly they started to slow down. This threw us. We had two choices—stay at the hospital and get induced with Oxytocin (a hormone that causes contractions of the uterus) or go back home and wait until the evening. Of course, Leigha decided to induce her labour. She couldn't bear going back home; it was time to finally get this show on the road.

Once Leigha was induced around 11:00 am, everything seemed to happen at lightning speed. Her contractions came on hard and fast. Being a pro, she handled them exceptionally well. Witnessing it firsthand and up close, I'm in awe of anyone who gives birth. The tenacity and strength women have during childbirth is simply incredible. And I must admit, I now get the joke about how if men could give birth, there would be hardly any children born.

With Josh firmly holding her hand on one side and Leigha's best friend Nicole on the other, it wasn't long before Dr Jensen was asking Leigha to do some final pushes and saying he could see the head. Ryan, Mum and I couldn't stop crying. Thank goodness for the person who invented waterproof mascara. And then we heard him cry. His first beautiful cry. He was here. After six years, our long-awaited darling son was finally here.

"Would you like to touch him?" Dr Jensen gently asked, motioning us towards him. The words we had been aching to hear for years. Our eyes flooded with tears, Ryan and I stumbled over and held Spencer's tiny hand while he lay on Leigha's stomach. In that moment, we knew it had all been worth it.

Ryan cut the umbilical cord and then our obstetrician and midwife did the Apgar score to check Spencer's general condition and vitals. Nine out of ten, he was safe and healthy. They then wrapped Spencer in a warm towel and brought him over to us. I had worn a hospital gown Leigha had given me so that Spencer could lay on my chest and nestle in, a beautiful moment I'll always remember. I once read a quote from Jimmy Fallon about his surrogacy journey and it perfectly captures how I felt in that moment: "...just hang in there...Try every avenue, try anything you can do, because you'll get there. You'll end up with a family, and it's so worth it. It is the most 'worth it' thing". He was right, it is the most 'worth it' thing.

Leigha wrote a beautiful piece for the blog of our fertility clinic (Utah Fertility Center) about her experience as a surrogate for Spencer. I encourage you to read her full story at utahfertility. com, but here's an extract of her experience about the day Spencer was born:

> *And before we knew it, Spencer John Wilson was here. I remember looking over at his loving parents and nanny Sue and the look of love and joy through all the tears. It had a beautiful peace about it. I was lucky to have my husband and best friend Nicole by my side as well as my wonderful and compassionate doctor. I can never thank Dr. Adam Jensen in Gunnison, Utah, and his awesome staff for not only being there for me every step of this journey, but they were also there for me through my first one as well.*
>
> *Now, after a few complications (because why not?) and a long night of small check-ups and tests, we all went home as a new big family. I now have two beautiful families that complete my family. One in Spain and now, another in Australia. They will always be a part of me, and I'm so blessed to have two sisters through motherhood. It was hard to put everything into so few words, but If you take anything from this, don't give up. I truly believe things happen for a reason, and regardless of if you ever find out the reason or not, the journey makes it worth the story.*

For the next half hour, we all held him. We savoured every moment, we soaked it all up. People had told us how you instantly fall in love with your child. I never really understood that—to love someone you had only just met—until that day.

I remember walking over to Leigha and crying, both of us saying we loved each other. I then looked over to Ryan and saw him marvelling at Spencer, looking mesmerised. He later told me that while he held Spencer close to his chest and they both stared at each other, he had never felt so happy and peaceful in his life. He told me it was the best day of his life. I believed him. Although I didn't have the heart to tell him Spencer wouldn't have been able to see him at that point.

Leigha and I spoke many times about why she chose to be a gestational surrogate. It's something we still talk about today. It's a massive commitment and not something many women could, or would want to, do. For Leigha, there were a few reasons. When she was younger, she was told she would have a difficult time carrying a baby to term because of a hormone imbalance. When she tried to first get pregnant, her obstetrician had worked with many women with this issue, and he was able to help her. He didn't consider it a problem, despite what she had been told by her previous doctor. But before knowing it wasn't an issue, she experienced the fear many women struggling with infertility have: 'Will I ever be a mum?' That feeling had stayed with her.

Years later, her friend Amy carried twins for a family. Amy expressed to Leigha the joy she had being a surrogate. This made Leigha curious. Not knowing too much about it, she started to research surrogacy. And once she started down this path, Leigha says there was no turning back. It felt like surrogacy was something she was destined to do.

About thirty minutes after Spencer was born, the midwife ushered us into our adjoining room so that Dr Jensen could check Leigha and we could feed Spencer. A few moments later, it was pandemonium. We saw an OR team (Emergency team) rush into Leigha's room. Ryan quickly followed but was told to wait outside as Leigha had started to bleed out. With Spencer resting quietly in my arms, I prayed she would be okay. Dr Jensen calmly took charge and stopped the bleeding. It was scary there for a while as Leigha lost more than 1.5 litres of blood. But she was okay and safe in the end. In the days that followed, she also experienced Postpartum Preeclampsia, a rare condition that causes high blood pressure and excess protein in your urine. It requires immediate treatment with medication and monitoring. If left untreated, it can cause seizures or other serious complications. For Leigha, it was causing painful headaches, swelling, bloating and dizziness. It was another reminder of the extraordinary gift Leigha had given us. She had risked her life for us, for Spencer. We felt an overwhelming sense of gratitude and love.

The next day, the four of us were discharged from the hospital. In the lead up to Spencer's birth, I did what most first-time parents do. I read a stack of parenting books and listened to podcasts. I was informed. I was ready. If only it was that easy. I soon learned that nothing really prepares you for a baby. Luckily, we had Leigha and Josh to guide us and offer us some "tips and tricks", as Leigha would say. We made the usual mistakes of course, like not fastening on his nappy tight enough and being peed on all over (more than once). Where was that in the books? But Leigha was there every step of the way to help us.

CHAPTER 13: COMING HOME

You are my sun, my moon, and all my stars (E.E. Cummings)

While we settled into our new role as parents, we also had to prepare for our trip home.

The first step was fast tracking Spencer's birth certificate and applying for his U.S. passport. Another benefit of surrogacy in the U.S. is dual citizenship. Spencer even has his own social security card. We organised his Australian citizenship a few weeks later, once we were back home, through an immigration lawyer. Our lawyer had mentioned that given Spencer was one hundred per cent genetically our baby, this would expedite the process. He was right. It only took a couple of weeks for Spencer to become an Australian citizen. We then applied for his Australian passport. Our lawyer was quick to manage our expectations. He told us that as the Immigration Department (responsible for his citizenship) and the Australian Passport Office don't 'talk to each other', and this meant that his proof of citizenship wasn't a guarantee that Spencer would automatically receive an Australian passport. This made us nervous, but thankfully he was soon issued an Australian passport.

For Spencer's U.S. passport, trying to get his passport photo was about as challenging as you would expect. Especially as his eyes needed to be open and he couldn't be crying. Sleeping and crying were the only two things Spencer was mastering at this point. It took us half an hour. That may not sound too long but have you ever tried to take the one perfect photo of a baby in the same spot for thirty minutes? Trust me, it feels long. We also visited our obstetrician to check Spencer's general health. Being first time parents, we may have gone a few more times than we needed to. But it was a long flight home and we had precious cargo with us.

The next three weeks in Gunnison flew by and before we knew it, it was time to say goodbye. It was a moment I had been quietly dreading since Leigha first fell pregnant. We had known each other now for eighteen months. And for nine of those months, we had shared something so life changing and intimate. I considered Leigha like a sister, and I knew when we said goodbye, it would be a long time until we saw each other again. The night before we left, Leigha gave us a beautiful gift, a scrapbook of our journey together. From the IVF transfer and positive pregnancy result through to our time in Gunnison and Spencer's birth, it was all in there. Looking through the book, I cried. It is one of my most cherished gifts and I look forward to the day when we can walk Spencer through this special book, a testament to him.

To avoid a big tearful farewell, Leigha's good friend Nicole, who had been at Spencer's birth, picked her up from home a couple of hours before we left for the airport. I understood why. Saying goodbye to Leigha and Josh was incredibly hard. With tears rolling down my face as I tightly hugged Leigha, I thought to myself, how do I say goodbye to someone who has come into our life and changed it so profoundly? Who has helped give us the greatest gift of all? But I told myself it wasn't forever. A few months after we arrived home, we booked a trip to visit Leigha and Josh for when Spencer would be ten months old. But sadly, Covid-19 thwarted our plans. We were all so disappointed we couldn't see each other. But I know we will definitely reunite in the next couple of years, and I can't wait until that day.

Our flight home from Los Angeles was sixteen hours (not including our two-hour flight from Salt Lake City to LA). A few people had teased, "You're game to travel on a long flight with a newborn!" Not that we had a choice. Now that we were parents, FedEx didn't seem like a responsible option. Walking through the airplane aisle to find our seats though, we received plenty of dirty looks. And some pity looks. I honestly didn't know which were worse. But for the most part, Spencer slept soundly to the gentle vibrations of the plane engine.

We arrived back home on 29 July 2019. Ryan's parents and my dad greeted us at the airport. It was an emotional reunion, full of tears and laughter. Spencer was the first grandchild for both our parents, and our miracle baby. Our families had been so invested in our journey. They had shared our highs but also our disappointments and heartbreak. As our parents, I know they would have experienced dark days of their own during our journey. I remember on one surrogacy cycle that had failed, I called Dad and he burst into tears. He could hardly talk so he handed the phone quickly over to Mum.

I remember a similar incident with Ryan's mum except this time it was about good news. Sadly, it was our surrogacy cycle that resulted in a miscarriage, but when we first received the positive pregnancy test result, she called me and broke down. You could tell she was so happy and relieved. I remember her voice breaking as she tearfully cried over and over, "Wonderful news, this is just great. Just great. It's just great". So, I can only imagine the crushing low she would have experienced when Ryan called her the very next month to say we had lost our baby.

But the day we arrived home, there was only light and pure joy. Ryan often jokes how his parents almost knocked us over to get to Spencer. I have a photo capturing the moment at the airport when Ryan's parents first met Spencer and Spencer met his grandparents. Their eyes full of happiness, love and pride, both grinning from ear to ear. A moment I'm sure they'll never forget. In the weeks that followed, there was a procession of visitors. Everyone was dying to meet this long-awaited and treasured baby.

It took us six years, one month and five days to have our beautiful son Spencer. A long and often difficult journey. But would I have changed it? How would our life look if it had taken us one month to conceive Spencer and not years?

It may have taken us years, but the day Spencer was born, most of the heartbreak and grief melted away. I had heard this from a friend who had battled infertility. That the day you have your baby safely resting in your arms, nearly all the pain vanishes. While I was sceptical, the mere thought of this was always a warm comfort. And she was right. For years, I had cried more than I ever thought was possible. I had cursed the universe and felt the bitter sting of grief time and time again. And then on 5 July 2019 at 11:49 am, it was as if the pain had never existed. As if I had never cried a tear. The bubble had finally burst. We were in a new place now.

I would be lying if I said all the pain has gone or that I

wouldn't have changed anything. And that's what happened in Canada. People often say that everything happens for a reason. I'm not convinced that's always true. Not only was it extremely painful but it's also left a mark that won't seem to go away. While most of the hurt of those six years has disappeared, there are days when I think about 'The Canada Event' and I anxiously brace myself for 'something' unexpectedly to go wrong. I've been told this may be a form of post-traumatic stress. Because before Canada, I never felt this way.

I always try hard to put this notion out of my mind, but it's always there, festering away. This feeling does lessen with each passing year, but I'm not sure it will ever completely go away. Or it's something I'll have to work on. I do remind myself we could never have predicted what happened in Canada. And that's true of so many things in life. Why worry about things you can never predict? As the Baz Luhrmann song 'The Sunscreen Song' goes, "Don't worry about the future; or worry but know that worrying is as effective as trying to solve an algebra equation by chewing bubble gum. The real troubles in your life will always be things that never even crossed your worried mind".

Canada aside, I wouldn't have changed a thing. Michael Jordan once famously said that his late father taught him to always, "Take a negative and turn it into a positive".

I think MJ is onto something. There was a positive to come out of every negative. With each heartbreak or setback, Ryan and I grew closer. Every marriage, every relationship, will most likely endure a stormy period. For us, it was only about a year into our marriage when we really had to put those marriage vows to the test. It was hard at times, but I'm grateful that our marriage is stronger for it.

The other positives? I think for many people who endure a difficult or traumatic period in their lives, your sense of gratitude and empathy grows. And that's a gift. This experience has deepened my relationships with my friends and family and my gratitude for them. Also, no one is immune from suffering but when the day inevitably comes that we battle another difficult time in our lives,

I would like to think that my resilience is stronger now and that will help guide us through it. As Atticus Finch says in *To Kill a Mockingbird*, "I've never met a strong person with an easy past".

We also unexpectedly gained a new family, the beautiful Leigha and Josh and their two lovely sons. When we first embarked on our infertility journey, I would never have predicted we would join with another family, especially one on the other side of the world. I suppose that's what makes life great sometimes. The unexpected twists and turns, the wonderful surprises. The unexpected is not always a bad thing. It can be profound, beautiful and life changing.

So, on reflection, MJ is right. There are many positives that came out of the negatives.

And the greatest positive? It's Spencer, of course. And the immense gratitude and love we have for him. For the first six months of his life, not a day went by when I didn't burst into tears every morning when I picked him up out of his cot. I couldn't help myself. Overwhelmed with emotion, the tears always fell. The poor kid probably didn't know what to think as I saturated him with my salty tears. But I couldn't believe that he was here. That he was ours. That we had finally been blessed with a child. Our own little miracle.

Infertility can be brutal, raw and often lonely. But for anyone struggling with infertility, you are not alone. I know it can sometimes feel that way. I know I felt that way. But there are many of us out there. Find those people. Talk to them. Lean on them. Surround yourself with love and support. Don't suffer in silence.

As I finish writing our story, Spencer is two years old. He is full of energy, has the most infectious cheeky smile and laugh and is the love of our lives. I know we had our rocky times over our six-year journey, but I want to thank you, universe. Thank you for giving us the most precious and beautiful person in our world. We will be forever grateful.

ACKNOWLEDGEMENTS

First and foremost, I want to thank my dad, John McLennan, for strongly encouraging me to write this book and share my story. Your constant support, love, professional guidance and valuable feedback brought this story to life.

To my husband Ryan Wilson, thank you for your unwavering encouragement and positivity as I penned our story. And thank you for the love you give me every single day.

To the people who supported me writing this book and offered me valuable guidance. In particular—family friend and author of *Olympia* John A. Martino; co-founder of *IVF babble* Sara Marshall-Page; and C&R Press Publisher & Editorial Directors Andrew Ibis and John Gosslee and the wonderful team at C&R Press.

To the many people who supported us during our infertility journey. To our parents (my parents, John and Suzan, and Ryan's parents, Kim and Steve); siblings (my sister Amy and Ryan's sister Amy and his brother Adam); Ryan's nan Jean; and our friends. Thank you for your endless support and love as we navigated this difficult time in our lives for several years.

To all the doctors, nurses, counsellors and specialists for your care and professional guidance. In particular— Russell A. Foulk, MD, Medical Director/Founder, Utah Fertility Center, and all the amazing staff at the Utah Fertility Center; and our obstetrician Dr. Adam Jensen and the wonderful staff at the Gunnison Valley Hospital.

Finally, a heartfelt thank you to our beautiful gestational surrogate Leigha and her family (her husband Josh and their two sons, JJ and Tyler). Leigha, we can't thank you enough for helping us bring Spencer into this world. You have brought so much happiness into our lives and into the lives of our loved ones. We are so blessed to have met you and we will be forever grateful.

GLOSSARY OF TERMS

Acupuncture. A complementary medical practice that stimulates certain points on the body—using tiny needles—to help ease pain or treat various health conditions. With infertility, it's meant to boost blood flow to reproductive organs and balance hormones.

Altruistic surrogacy. A surrogate carries a child for another person or persons, but she does not receive monetary compensation. Only out of pocket expenses are covered.

Advanced Maternal Age (AMA). A pregnancy may be considered higher risk due to AMA. A woman of AMA may be more likely than a younger woman to have certain conditions and complications that may put her and the baby at risk.

Anti-Mullerian Hormone (AMH). A hormone secreted by cells in developing egg sacs (follicles). The level of AMH in blood helps predict a women's remaining egg maturation potential (ovarian reserve) and her likelihood of conceiving.

Apgar score. The Apgar score is a measure of a baby's condition after birth. A score of seven or more is considered normal. More information: Pregnancybirthbaby.org.au.

Balanced translocation. A chromosome breaks and a portion of it reattaches to a different chromosome. Sections of the two chromosomes have switched places. In four per cent of all couples with recurrent miscarriage, one or even both parents have a balanced translocation. More information: verywellfamily.com

Blastocyst embryo. An advanced stage of embryological development. The embryo has developed for five to seven days after fertilisation and has two distinct cell types and a central cavity filled with fluid. More information: advancedfertility.com

Braxton Hicks contractions. Often known as false labour pains, they are contractions of a women's uterus in preparation for giving birth.

Clexane injections. Clexane is a blood thinning drug that increases blood flow and helps prevent blood clots.

Clomiphene (Clomid). A medication used to treat infertility in women who do not ovulate. This includes women who have polycystic ovary syndrome. More information: healthline.com

Cognitive Behavioural Therapy (CBT). CBT focuses on challenging and changing unhelpful thoughts, beliefs, attitudes and behaviours, and developing personal coping strategies that target solving current problems. More information: Change your Thinking, Dr Sarah Edelman.

Commercial surrogacy. Commercial surrogacy is an arrangement whereby the surrogate is compensated beyond just reimbursement of medical expenses by payment of a fee.

Dilation and Curettage (D&C). "Dilation" refers to opening the cervix and the "curette" refers to removing the contents of the uterus. A D&C is performed to clear the uterine lining after a miscarriage.

Donor egg or embryo. For women who are unable to conceive using their own eggs, they can use a donor egg or embryo. More information: webmd.com

Egg fertilisation. The eggs must be fertilised quickly. There are two fertilisation methods: conventional insemination or Intra Cytoplasmic Sperm Injection (ICSI). Conventional insemination involves healthy sperm and mature eggs mixed in a petri dish and incubated overnight. Refer to ICIS in Glossary for definition.

Egg retrieval surgery. A hospital day procedure to collect eggs from a women's ovaries. Under general anaesthetic, an ultrasound probe is inserted into the woman's vaginal wall to identify follicles and then a needle is guided through. The needle goes into each of the ovarian follicles and gentle suction is used to pull out the fluid and the egg that comes with it.

Embryo grading system (Blastocyst embryos). Blastocyst embryos are graded ABC. A has many well-defined and smooth cells. In contrast, C has few cells, and they are dark and irregular. More information: advancedferitlity.com

Embryologist

A fertility specialist that helps to create viable embryos to either be used in IVF right away or to be frozen for later use.

Endometriosis

A disorder in which tissue that normally lines the uterus grows outside the uterus. Approximately a third of women with endometriosis have trouble conceiving. More information: pregnancybirthbaby.org.au

Endometrium lining

The endometrium is the innermost lining layer of the uterus. One of the stars of the female reproductive system, it plays a key role during pregnancy. The endometrium is the wallpaper of the uterus and with pregnancy, it becomes thicker so that it's ready to receive an embryo and support the placenta. The placenta is the organ that develops during pregnancy to provide the baby with oxygen, blood and nutrients.

Endometrial Receptivity Array (ERA)

A genetic test where a small sample of a woman's endometrial lining is taken to identify the best day and time to transfer an embryo for pregnancy. Approximately twenty-five per cent of women transfer on the wrong day. More information: igenomix.com

Endometrial scratching

A technique used to improve the ability of an embryo to implant in the uterus after IVF. It involves superficially wounding the lining of the womb to improve the receptivity of the uterus to the embryo.

Estrogen. In preparation for pregnancy, the hormone estrogen increases blood flow to a women's uterus. This grows and maintains the endometrium lining.

Ectopic pregnancy. A fertilised egg implants itself outside the womb, generally in one of the fallopian tubes. More information: pregnancybirthbaby.org.au

Families Through Surrogacy. A consumer-based non-profit organisation in Australia, supporting intended parents and surrogates. More information: familiesthrusurrogacy.com

Foetal anomaly scan. This ultrasound looks in detail at a baby's bones, heart, organs and checks the position of the placenta, and umbilical cord. The ultrasound is performed at twenty weeks.

Foetal heartbeat. A foetal heartbeat may first be detected by a vaginal ultrasound around six weeks after gestation. More information: healthline.com

Follicles. A follicle is a sac filled with fluid in which an immature egg develops. Follicles are in the ovaries. When a follicle grows to an ideal size, ovulation occurs.

Gestational Carrier. A Gestational Carrier is a woman who carries and delivers a child for another couple or person, known as the intended parent(s). They are either pregnant with the parent's genetic embryo, or a donor egg or embryo.

Gonal-f. A follicle stimulating hormone. Usually, each month the body naturally releases one mature egg. On rare occasions, two eggs. Gonal-f helps to stimulate a women's ovaries to over produce eggs.

Human chorionic gonadotropin (hCG). A hormone produced by your placenta once an embryo implants in the uterus. More information: pregnancybirthbaby.org.au

Intra Cytoplasmic Sperm Injection (ICSI). A technique where a single sperm is injected directly into the centre of the egg. More information: monashivf.com.

Intrauterine Insemination (IUI). A process of injecting sperm directly into a women's uterus using a catheter. More information: ivf.com.au

In Vitro Fertilisation (IVF). A procedure, used to overcome a range of fertility issues, in which an egg and sperm are joined together outside the body, in a specialised laboratory. The fertilised egg (embryo) is allowed to grow in a protected environment for some days before being transferred into the woman's uterus increasing the chance that a pregnancy will occur.

Laparoscopy. A keyhole surgery to examine, or operate, on the interior of the abdominal or pelvic cavities. A laparoscopy has all the usual side effects of abdominal pain, nausea, light-headedness and sometimes a persistent cough and shortness of breath.

Methotrexate. A chemotherapy agent to treat cancer, autoimmune diseases and ectopic pregnancies.

Miscarriage. The spontaneous loss of a women's pregnancy before twenty weeks of pregnancy. Up to one in five confirmed pregnancies end in miscarriage.

Missed miscarriage. Also known as a silent miscarriage, this occurs when a foetus is no longer alive, but the body does not recognise the pregnancy loss or expel the pregnancy tissue.

Orgalutran. This medication is used to prevent premature ovulation. Side effects include headache, nausea, dizziness and irritation/redness at the injection site.

Ovarian Hyper Stimulation Syndrome (OHSS). OHSS is a side effect of IVF stimulation medication. The ovaries become very enlarged with fluid, causing abdominal pain and bloating. More information: mayoclinic.org.

Ovidrel. A fertility medication used to trigger ovulation. More information: healthline.com

Oxytocin. A hormone that causes contractions of the uterus. Oxytocin is used to induce labour.

Pre-Genetic Screening (PGS) testing. PGS tests if your embryos are genetically normal. It screens embryos to ensure they have the correct number and order of chromosomes. This includes twenty-three pairs of chromosomes. If a chromosome is missing or duplicated, an embryo won't implant. More information: utahfertility.com

Pregnancy of an Unknown Location (PUL). A pregnancy test is positive but there are no signs of intrauterine pregnancy via transvaginal ultrasound. It is not always possible to determine the location of the pregnancy.

Pre-birth order (surrogacy). Both the surrogate and intended parent(s) assign parentage to the intended parents and remove any rights or obligations from the surrogate. This order allows parentage to the intended parent(s) before the child is even born.

Polycystic ovaries

Refers to an ultrasound image of the ovaries that appear to be polycystic, i.e., ovaries containing high density of partially mature follicles.

Poly Cystic Ovaries Syndrome (PCOS). The Syndrome is a complex hormonal condition. You produce eggs but you don't always ovulate. It leaves your ovaries filled with follicles which have 'failed to launch'. There are also some unpleasant symptoms like excess facial and body hair, acne, and mood changes. It affects approximately fifteen per cent of women.

Progesterone. A hormone that helps the fertilised egg be implanted in the uterus to establish a pregnancy and maintain it. Women naturally produce progesterone in the ovaries. During IVF, progesterone is given because IVF medication reduces a woman's natural production of the hormone.

Postpartum Preeclampsia. A rare condition that causes high blood pressure and excess protein in a women's urine. It requires immediate treatment with medication and monitoring. If left untreated, it can cause seizures or other serious complications.

Subchorionic hematoma. A blood clot that is formed by the abnormal collection of blood between the placenta and the wall of the uterus. Occasionally a hematoma can grow and cause miscarriage, preterm labour or placental abruptions.

Traditional surrogate. A traditional surrogate is not only a carrier as she also uses her own eggs. Although these days, traditional surrogacy is rare.

Transporting embryos. To transport embryos, they are kept at a consistent temperature (temperature needs to stay at below -150 degrees) in cryo-storage tanks filled with liquid nitrogen. More information: corecryolab.com

Transfer procedure. For the transfer, an embryologist prepares the embryo by placing it in a catheter. Under guided ultrasound, the fertility specialist then threads the catheter up through the woman's cervix and into her uterus. More information: utahfertility.com

VARTA (Victorian Assisted Reproductive Treatment Authority). The key regulation body in Victoria, Australia. A statutory authority, VARTA provides independent information and support to people about fertility treatments.

REFERENCES

CHAPTER 1

"A journey of a thousand miles": Lao Tzu, *Tao Te Ching*, 4th or 5th century.

"The very least you can do in your life is figure out what you hope for": Barbara Kingsolver, 199, *Animal Dreams*, United States.

CHAPTER 2

"Don't worry about failures": Jack Canfield, 1993, *Chicken Soup for the Soul*, United States.

A normal ovarian reserve count is six to ten follicles: January 2020, 'What are follicles & how many are normal in each ovary?' *Fertility family*, https://www.fertilityfamily.co.uk/blog/how-many-eggs-per-follicle-everything-you-need-to know

Up to a third of women have polycystic ovaries seen on an ultrasound: October 2018, 'Polycystic ovaries vs Polycystic Ovarian Syndrome', *Dr Omar Gailani Blog*, https://www.omargailani.com.au/blog/polycystic-ovaries-vs-polycystic-ovarian-syndrome-13783/

Poly Cystic Ovaries Syndrome affects approximately fifteen per cent of women: 'What you should know about polycystic ovarian syndrome in pregnancy', *healthline*, https://www.healthline.com/health/pregnancy/pcos

On average, women under thirty-five; For women over forty: Sarah Kelsey, March 2019, 'What I wish I'd known before my first IUI', *Today's Parent*, https://www.todaysparent.com/getting-pregnant/infertility/what-i-wish-id-known-before-my-first-iui/

CHAPTER 3

"Never give up on something": Winston Churchill, October

1941, 'Never Give In speech', Harrow School, UK.

So, what is In Vitro Fertilisation (IVF)?: IVF Australia definition, https://www.ivf.com.au/treatments/fertility-treatments/ivf-treatment

In Australia over the past forty years: Alannah Frost, June 2020, 'Making Miracles', *Herald Sun.*

According to the Australian and New Zealand Assisted Reproduction Database: Jade Newman et al., September 2020, 'Assisted reproductive technology in Australia and New Zealand 2018', *National Perinatal Epidemiology & Statistics Unit.*

In the United States: Maya Dusenbery, 9 November 2021, 'What we don't know about IVF', *New York Times.*

Prices differ according to country: IVF Australia, https://www.ivf.com.au/ivf-cost/ivf-costs

Today, it's estimated that one in six couples worldwide battle infertility: IVF Australia, https://www.ivf.com.au/planning-for-pregnancy/what-is-infertility

According to the World Health Organisation: World Health Organisation definition. 'Infertility', https://www.who.int/health-topics/infertility#tab=tab_1

In one particular study, it showed that infertile women experience: Kristin L. Rooney and Alice D. Domar, March 2018, 'The relationship between stress and infertility', *Dialogues in clinical neuroscience*, Boston.

The ABC News article: Sophie Scott and Angela McCormack, January 2020, 'IVF is big business in Australia—but these people are calling the industry out', *ABC News*, Australia.

I once read a witty piece in Mamamia: Donna Dunn, October 2012, 'The things you don't want to hear when you're doing IVF', *Mamamia*, Australia.

The Australian and New Zealand Assisted Reproduction Database (ANZARD) report: Olivia Willis, September 2019,

'IVF success rate improve amid growing concerns about lack of industry transparency', *ABC News*, Australia.

Women make up around forty per cent of all the treated infertility cases in Australia: 'Infertility statistics and facts for Australian couples', *fertility solutions*, https://fertilitysolutions.com. au/infertility-statistics/

On average, around sixty to seventy per cent of mature eggs will fertilise: Sharon Mazel, April 2020, 'In Vitro Fertilisation (IVF)', *What to expect*, https://www.whattoexpect.com/getting-pregnant/ivf/

For blastocyst embryos, ninety per cent: 'Frozen embryo transfer', *Life Fertility Clinic,* https://www.lifefertility.com.au/ resources/factsheets/frozen-embryo-transfer/

In 2019, a global study: Sophie Scott, 23 January 2019, 'IVF scratching: Are women putting themselves through a painful procedure for nothing?, *ABC News,* Australia.

One of the stars of the female reproductive system: Tracee Cornforth, 25 November 2020, 'The role the endometrium plays in your reproductive health', *verywellhealth*

One research study showed that with a lining: Michael von Wolff et al., December 2018, 'Thin Endometrium is also associated with lower clinical pregnancy rate in unstimulated menstrual cycles: A study based on natural cycle IVF', *Front Endocrinol,* 9: 776.

The lining—One of the stars of the female reproductive system: Tracey Cornforth and Anita Sadaty, January 2020, 'The role of the endometrium plays in your reproductive health', *very well health,* https://www.verywellhealth.com/what-is-the-endometrium-2721857

To put it in perspective, a women's lining starts at 3mm: https://advancedfertility.com/patient-education/;

A study published in the British Medical Journal: Eric Manheimer et al., 2008, 'Effects of acupuncture on rates of pregnancy and live birth among women undergoing in vitro fertilisation: systematic review and meta-analysis', *British Medical Journal,* 336(7643): 545-9.

In contrast, an Australian landmark study: Caroline Smith, Sheryl de Lacey, Michael Chapman, May 2018, 'Effect of Acupuncture vs shame Acupuncture on lives births among women undergoing In Vitro Fertilisation', *Journal of the American Medical Association,* 319(19): 1990-1998.

CHAPTER 4

"If your nerve deny you—Go above your nerve": Emily Dickinson, 1935, 'If Your Nerve Deny You' (292).

As hCG needs to at least double every forty-eight hours: 'hCG levels and miscarriage', *healthline,* https://www.healthline.com/health/hcg-levels-miscarriage

I quickly Googled it and came across a leaflet: 'Pregnancy of an Unknown Location', 2017, *North Bristol NHS,* https://www.nbt.nhs.uk/sites/default/files/attachments/Pregnancy%20of%20unknown%20location_NBT002001.pdf

Infertility in the workplace is still not openly discussed: @ fertilitymattersatwork Instagram account.

The World Health Organisation defines infertility: World Health Organisation definition. 'Infertility', https://www.who.int/health-topics/infertility#tab=tab_1

I once watched a TV interview: Dr Russell Foulk, 26 November 2011, *Good Things Utah,* United States.

CHAPTER 5

"Always forward, never back": Junipero Serra.

Earlier on I read an article: Shannon Firth, 30 January 2014, 'Study: Infertile couples 3 times more likely to divorce', *U.S. News.*

OHSS is a side effect of IVF stimulation medication: 'Ovarian hyperstimulation syndrome', https://www.mayoclinic.org/ diseases-conditions/ovarian-hyperstimulation-syndrome-ohss/ symptoms-causes/syc-20354697

If a chromosome is missing or duplicated: 'PGS Embryo screening', Genea, https://www.genea.com.au/assisted-concep tion/genetic-testing/pgd-genetic-test

Also, a pregnancy rate on a PGS cycle is sixty to seventy per cent: 'CCRM fertility success rates', *CCRM Fertility,* https://www. ccrmivf.com/fertility-success-rates/

CHAPTER 6

"No one ever told me that grief felt so much like fear": C.S Lewis, 1961, *A Grief Observed*, Faber & Faber, United Kingdom.

It's estimated that fifteen per cent of confirmed pregnancies: Stacy A. Henigsman and Zawn Villines, 2021, 'What are the average miscarriage rates by week?', *Medical News Today,* https:// www.medicalnewstoday.com/articles/322634.

CBT focuses on challenging and changing: 'All About Cognitive Behavioural Therapy', *PsychCentral,* https:// psychcentral.com/lib/in-depth-cognitive-behavioral-therapy

Change your thinking: Dr Sarah Edelman, 2006, *Change Your Thinking*, Ebury Publishing, Great Britain.

CHAPTER 7

"Hope is a waking dream": Aristotle.

First IVF baby: 'Louise Brown, World's first IVF baby's family archive unveiled', July 2018, *BBC News.*

The success rate with PGS embryos and surrogacy is eighty per cent: William Houghton, 'Understanding surrogacy success rates', *The Surrogate Mother's Guide,* https://www.sensiblesurrogacy.

com/surrogacy-success-rates/

CHAPTER 8

"History doesn't repeat itself, but it does rhyme": Mark Twain (attributed)

Resilience is defined as: 'Resilience: Build skills to endure hardship', *Mayo Clinic,* https://www.mayoclinic.org/tests-procedures/resilience-training/in-depth/resilience/art-20046311

CHAPTER 9

"Fall down seven times": Japanese proverb.

Dad was diagnosed with 'diffuse large B-cell': 'What is Diffuse large B-cell lymphoma (DLBCL)?', *Leukaemia Foundation,* https://www.leukaemia.org.au/blood-cancer-information/types-of-blood-cancer/lymphoma/non-hodgkin-lymphoma/diffuse-large-b-cell-lymphoma/

CHAPTER 10

"Hope smiles from the threshold": Alfred Tennyson, 1891, Act I, Scene III, *The Foresters.*

The US boasts the highest surrogacy success: William Houghton, 'Understanding Surrogacy Success Rates', *The Surrogate Mother's Guide,* https://www.sensiblesurrogacy.com/surrogacy-success-rates/

The cost ranges from US$90,000-150,000: Susannah Snider, 'The Cost of Using a Surrogate', 24 November 2020, *U.S. News*

In Michigan for example: 'Guide to State Surrogacy Laws', December 2007, *Centre for American Progress,* https://www.americanprogress.org/article/guide-to-state-surrogacy-laws/

Ninety-two per cent of babies are born overseas: Sam G Everingham, Martyn A Stafford-Bell and Karin Hammarberg, August 2014, 'Australians' use of surrogacy', *The Medical Journal of Australia*, 201(5): 270-273.

According to the Australian Government 'Smart Traveller': 'Going overseas for international surrogacy', *Smart Traveller*, https://www.smartraveller.gov.au/before-you-go/activities/surrogacy

For the Utah Fertility Center: 'IVF success rates', Utah Fertility Center, https://www.utahfertility.com/treatmentivf/advanced-techniques-ivf/ivf-success-rates/

In 2019, there was a story on Foreign Correspondent: Samantha Hawley, August 2019, 'Damaged babies and broken hearts: Ukraine's commercial surrogacy industry leaves a trail of disasters', *Foreign Correspondent, ABC*.

It is half the typical miscarriage rate: Dr Owen Davis and Jamie Grifo MD, 'The benefits of PGS', *FertilityIQ*, http://www.fertilityiq.com.

He explained how twenty-five per cent of women transfer: Dr Laurence Jacobs, 2 September 2015 'ERA test finds 25% of IVF Frozen transfers occur on wrong day', *Fertility Centers of Illinois*.

An ERA is a genetic test: 'What is an ERA Test and How it Can Help You', July 2017, *Igenomix*, https://www.igenomix.pe/fertility-challenges/what-is-an-era-test-and-how-it-can-help-you/

CHAPTER 11

"In the midst of winter...": Albert Camus, 1942, *The Stranger*, France.

We had researched international adoption: 'Intercountry adoption Australia' (Australian Government), http://www.intercountryadoption.gov.au

Known as balanced translocation: Krissi Danielsson, May 2020,

'Balanced Translocation and Recurrent Miscarriage', *verywellfamily*, https://www.verywellfamily.com/balanced-translocation-and-recurrent-miscarriage-2371840

The chance of miscarrying from a haematoma: YT Huang, H Chen, JP Zhang, June 2018, 'Subchronic hematoma in a recurrent miscarriage population and the obstetric implications', *American Journal of Reproductive Immunology*.

He explained that in his experience: Christopher P. Bondick; Joe M Das; Howard Fertel, 22 November 2021, 'Subchorionic Hameorrhage', *NCBI*.

For Chinese adoption for example: 'Adopting a child from China, Intercountry Adoption Australia', https://www.intercountryadoption.gov.au/countries-and-considerations/countries/china/

"Family is not defined by our genes": Amalia G, The Children's Bridge Adoption Agency.

"Real courage is when you know": Harper Lee, 1960, *To Kill a Mockingbird*, United States.

CHAPTER 12

"It always seems impossible until it's done": Nelson Mandela.

Arizona in 2018- gender reveal fire: Joshua Rhett Miller, October 2018, 'Border Patrol agent admits starting massive wildfire at gender-reveal party', *New York Post*.

"…just hang in there": Aly Weisman, August 2013, 'Jimmy Fallon Reveals 'Awful' 5 Year Fertility Struggle Leading to Surrogate', *Business Insider Australia*.

CHAPTER 13

"As the Baz Luhrmann song 'The Sunscreen Song' goes…": Baz Luhrmann, 1997, 'The Sunscreen Song', *Something for Everybody*,

EMI, Capitol.

"I've never met a strong person with an easy past": Harper
Lee, 1960, *To Kill a Mockingbird*, United States.

C&R PRESS TITLES

NONFICTION

This is Infertility by Kirsten McLennan
Many Paths by Bruce McEver
By the Bridge or By the River by Amy Roma
Women in the Literary Landscape by Doris Weatherford, et al
Credo: An Anthology of Manifestos & Sourcebook for Creative Writing by Rita Banerjee and Diana Norma Szokolyai

FICTION

Transcendent Gardening by Ed Falco
Juniper Street by Joan Frank
All I Should Not Tell by Brian Leung
Last Tower to Heaven by Jacob Paul
History of the Cat in Nine Chapters or Less by Anis Shivani
No Good, Very Bad Asian by Lelund Cheuk
Surrendering Appomattox by Jacob M. Appel
Made by Mary by Laura Catherine Brown
Ivy vs. Dogg by Brian Leung
While You Were Gone by Sybil Baker
Cloud Diary by Steve Mitchell
Spectrum by Martin Ott
That Man in Our Lives by Xu Xi

SHORT FICTION

A Mother's Tale & Other Stories by Khanh Ha
Fathers of Cambodian Time-Travel Science by Bradley Bazzle
Two Californias by Robert Glick
Notes From the Mother Tongue by An Tran
The Protester Has Been Released by Janet Sarbanes

ESSAY AND CREATIVE NONFICTION

Selling the Farm by Debra Di Blasi
the internet is for real by Chris Campanioni
Immigration Essays by Sybil Baker
Death of Art by Chris Campanioni

POETRY

Curare by Lucian Mattison
Leaving the Skin on the Bear by Kelli Allen
How to Kill Yourself Instead of Your Children by Qunicy S. Jones
Lottery of Intimacies by Jonathan Katz
What Feels Like Love by Tom C. Hunley
The Rented Altar by Lauren Berry
Between the Earth and Sky by Eleanor Kedney
What Need Have We for Such as We by Amanda Auerbach
A Family Is a House by Dustin Pearson
The Miracles by Amy Lemmon
Banjo's Inside Coyote by Kelli Allen
Objects in Motion by Jonathan Katz
My Stunt Double by Travis Denton
Lessons in Camoflauge by Martin Ott
Millennial Roost by Dustin Pearson
All My Heroes are Broke by Ariel Francisco
Holdfast by Christian Anton Gerard
Ex Domestica by E.G. Cunningham
Like Lesser Gods by Bruce McEver
Notes from the Negro Side of the Moon by Earl Braggs
Imagine Not Drowning by Kelli Allen
Notes to the Beloved by Michelle Bitting
Free Boat: Collected Lies and Love Poems by John Reed
Les Fauves by Barbara Crooker
Tall as You are Tall Between Them by Annie Christain
The Couple Who Fell to Earth by Michelle Bitting
Notes to the Beloved by Michelle Bitting

Printed in Australia
AUHW020829181022
370357AU00007B/7